NEW BIBLE QUIZZES

Tests - Clues - Games

... By ...

J. VERNON JACOBS

Author of "Bible Quiz Book," etc.

THE STANDARD PUBLISHING COMPANY

CINCINNATI, OHIO, U. S. A.

Printed in U. S. A.

PREFACE

The widespread demand for "Bible quizzes," which sent the "Bible Quiz Book" into the fourth edition in a few months, has called for a companion volume of a similar nature.

It is not the purpose of this book to be a substitute for the Bible, but, rather, to create a new interest in the Bible by bringing to the attention of people the many interesting things contained therein. The better we know the Bible, the more sacred it becomes, and as we come to see that it meets our needs, the more likely we are to turn to it for guidance.

Following are suggestions for the use of the material in this volume:

Parties.—Choose sides, and allow the contestants to stand until a question is missed. It will be a matter of great satisfaction to an individual to feel that he was the final one to remain standing and thus is acknowledged to be the best Bible student in the group. Various games may be typed or mimeographed and handed to those present for filling in the answers or underscoring, as the case may be.

Evening Services.—A "quiz program," as a half-hour feature, preceding the sermon, is sure to bring increased attendance. Choose a half-dozen of your best Bible students, and give the program publicity through the church bulletin and city papers. Let the various groups in the Bible school appoint their best representatives to take part in it.

Young People will find quizzes an attractive item on any program in their evening meetings. It is also suggested that they challenge the young people in other churches to compete with them in a quiz contest.

Extended Sessions, or the Junior church, in which time is set apart for expressional activities, will find this material helpful. Children will enjoy the drills and "spell-downs," and will have a good time playing "Bible Baseball." Make a "diamond" by arranging four chairs, with one in the center for the "pitcher," who will ask the questions. If a child misses three questions, he is "out." If successful, he goes to the first chair, and is advanced by others, as in baseball.

Vacation Bible Schools will find an abundance of material for their expressional programs. A Bible quiz might be included in their demonstration program on the Sunday night following the close of the school.

We feel sorry for people who live in certain lands where the Bible is a forbidden Book, but the neglected Bible in a Christian land does one no more good than if there were none in the home. Let us cherish the Word of God, and become so well acquainted with it that it will indeed be "a lamp unto our feet and a light unto our path."

MEMPHIS, Tenn.   J. VERNON JACOBS.

NEW BIBLE QUIZZES

BIBLE ANIMALS—No. 1

Count ten points for each correct answer.

1. What forbidden animals did Solomon keep? .... □

2. On what kind of animals did 400 young Amalekites escape from David? .... □

3. What unclean animals were raised by the Gadarenes? □

4. When Gideon took his soldiers to the river, like what kind of animals did 300 of them drink? .... □

5. What prophet had a vision of a ram and a goat? □

6. What kind of tropical animals did Solomon import? □

7. What youth slew a lion and a bear? .... □

8. Who was the man that died from touching the ark when the oxen stumbled? .... □

9. Who said, "Can a leopard change his spots"? .... □

10. Who said, "Am I a dog that you come to me with staves"? .... □

Total score .... □

1. **Horses** (Deut. 17:16; 1 Kings 4:26); 2. **Camels** (1 Sam. 30:17); 3. **Swine** (Matt. 8:28-32); 4. **Dogs** (Judg. 7:5); 5. **Daniel** (Dan. 8:1-8); 6. **Apes** (2 Chron. 9:21); 7. **David** (1 Sam. 17:34); 8. **Uzzah** (2 Sam. 6:6); 9. **Jehovah** (Jer. 13:23); 10. **Goliath** (1 Sam. 17:43).

BIBLE ANIMALS—No. 2

Count ten points for each correct answer.

1. What animals are first mentioned as carrying mail? ☐

2. What animal did Jesus call Herod? .... ☐

3. What kind of animal did Israel worship at Mt. Sinai? ☐

4. When Abraham was about to offer up Isaac, what kind of animal was found in the thicket? .... ☐

5. When Rebekah came to marry Isaac, on what kind of animal was she riding? .... ☐

6. What kind of meat did Isaac like best? .... ☐

7. Who caught 300 foxes and set fire to their tails? .... ☐

8. What animal met Samson one day, and was slain by him? .... ☐

9. Who said, "Behold, the Lamb of God," in proclaiming Jesus? .... ☐

10. What animals are mentioned by Jesus in a parable of the judgment? .... ☐

Total score .... ☐

1. **Horses** (Esth. 8:10); 2. **Fox** (Luke 13:32); 3. **Calf** (Ex. 32:8); 4. **Ram** (Gen. 22:13); 5. **Camel** (Gen. 24:64); 6. **Venison** (Gen. 25:28); 7. **Samson** (Judg. 15:4); 8. **Lion** (Judg. 14:5, 6); 9. **John** (John 1:36); 10. **Sheep** and **Goats** (Matt. 25:31-36).

BIBLE BIRDS

1. What kind of bird did Noah first send out of the ark? ☐

2. What kind of birds brought food to Elijah? .... ☐

3. What kind of birds were sold "two for a farthing"? ☐

4. What kind of bird do we remember in connection with Simon Peter? .... ☐

5. What birds built nests on the altars of Jehovah? .... ☐

6. What kind of birds were sent to the Israelites for food? .... ☐

7. Jesus said He would have gathered the people of Jerusalem to Himself as what kind of a fowl gathered her little ones? .... ☐

8. What birds were used for sacrifices? .... ☐

9. David said our youth may be renewed as what kind of bird? .... ☐

10. When David complained of loneliness, he said he was like what kind of bird in the wilderness? .... ☐

Total score .... ☐

1. **Dove** (Gen. 8:8); 2. **Raven** (1 Kings 17:4-6); 3. **Sparrows** (Matt. 10:29); 4. **Cock** (Matt. 26:74); 5. **Sparrows** and **swallows** (Ps. 84:3); 6. **Quail** (Ex. 16:12, 13); 7. **Chicken** (Matt. 23:27); 8. **Pigeons** and **turtledoves** (Lev. 1:14); 9. **Eagle** (Ps. 103:5); 10. **Pelican** (Ps. 102:6).

BIBLE BOYS

1. What boy overheard a plot, and saved Paul's life? ☐

2. What boy refused to drink the king's wine? .... ☐

3. What boy died from sunstroke and was restored by Elisha? .... ☐

4. What boy got lost in Jerusalem, and His parents found Him in the temple? .... ☐

5. What boy began to reign as king at the age of seven? ☐

6. What boy was accused by his brothers of being naughty for wanting to see a battle? .... ☐

7. What boy nearly died of thirst in a desert? .... ☐

8. What boy helped Jesus to perform a miracle? .... ☐

9. What son of Janathan was left lame from an accident when five years of age? .... ☐

10. What boy grew up in the tabernacle from the time he was just an infant? .... ☐

Total score .... ☐

1. **Paul's nephew** (Acts 23:16); 2. **Daniel** (Dan. 1:8); 3. **The Shunammite's son** (2 Kings 4:18-37); 4. **Jesus** (Luke 2:41-52); 5. **Joash** (2 Kings 12:1); 6. **David** (1 Sam. 17:28); 7. **Ishmael** (Gen. 21:14-19); 8. **The boy with the loaves and fishes** (John 6:9-14); 9. **Mephibosheth** (2 Sam. 4:4); 10. **Samuel** (1 Sam. 3:1).

BIBLE CITIES—No. 1

1. What city is called "the city of David"? .... ☐

2. What city was given to Solomon by his father-in-law, Pharaoh? .... ☐

3. In what city did Elisha's servant see chariots of fire? ☐

4. On the walls of what city did the Philistines hang the bodies of Saul and his sons? .... ☐

5. In what city did Jesus have His headquarters? .... ☐

6. On what cities did God rain down fire? .... ☐

7. What was the "city of Mary and Martha"? .... ☐

8. Where did Goliath live? .... ☐

9. In what cities did Jeroboam place the golden calves? ☐

10. In what city did "an old witch" live? .... ☐

Total score .... ☐

1. **Bethlehem** (Luke 2:4); 2. **Gezer** (1 Kings 9:16); 3. **Dothan** (2 Kings 6:13-16); 4. **Beth-Shan** (1 Sam. 31:12); 5. **Capernaum** (Matt. 4:13); 6. **Sodom** and **Gomorrah** (Gen. 19:24); 7. **Bethany** (John 11:1); 8. **Gath** (1 Sam. 17:4); 9. **Dan** and **Bethel** (1 Kings 12:28, 29); 10. **Endor** (1 Sam. 28:7).

BIBLE CITIES—No. 2

1. What is the name of the first city built? .... ☐

2. What city was named for the confusion of tongues? ☐

3. Where did Ahab have his "ivory palace"? .... ☐

4. What city was called "the city of our God"? .... ☐

5. In what city did Demetrius start a riot? .... ☐

6. Over the wall of what city did Paul flee for his life? ☐

7. In what city were Paul and Barnabas mistaken for gods? .... ☐

8. What city is called "the city of the great king"? ☐

9. In what city was Paul born? .... ☐

10. What city is used as a type of heaven? .... ☐

Total score .... ☐

1. **Enoch** (Gen. 4:17); 2. **Babel** (Gen. 11:9); 3. **Samaria** (1 Kings 17:29; 22:39); 4. **Jerusalem** (Ps. 48:1); 5. **Ephesus** (Acts 19:24); 6. **Damascus** (Acts 9:25); 7. **Lystra** (Acts 14:11); 8. **Jerusalem** (Ps. 48:2); 9. **Tarsus** (Acts 9:11); 10. **Jerusalem** (Rev. 21:2).

BIBLE MOTHERS

Count ten points for each correct answer.

1. Eve was the mother of Noah? Seth? Enoch? .... ☐

2. Sarah was the mother of Ishmael? Isaac? Dan? ...... ☐

3. Rebekah was the mother of Esau? Joseph?
   Shadrach? .... ☐

4. Rachel was the mother of Cain? Saul? Benjamin? ☐

5. Jochebed was the mother of Moses? Levi? Jonah? ☐

6. Hannah was the mother of John? Solomon?
   Samuel? .... ☐

7. Abi was the mother of Jeroboam? Asa? Hezekiah? ☐

8. Elisabeth was the mother of Peter? Jesus? John? ☐

9. Eunice was the mother of Philip? Timothy? Paul? ☐

10. Ruth was the mother of Obed? Jesse? David? .... ☐

Total score .... ☐

1. **Seth** (Gen. 4:5); 2. **Isaac** (Gen. 21:3); 3. **Esau** (Gen. 27:42); 4. **Benjamin** (Gen. 35:24); 5. **Moses** (Ex. 6:20); 6. **Samuel** (1 Sam. 1:20); 7. **Hezekiah** (2 Kings 18:2); 8. **John** (Luke 1:57-63); 9. **Timothy** (2 Tim. 1:6); 10. **Obed** (Ruth 4:17).

BIBLE RIVERS—No. 1

Count ten points for each correct answer.

1. In what river was Jesus baptized? .... ☐

2. What rivers bounded the land given to Abraham by Jehovah? .... ☐

3. What were the rivers of Damascus which Naaman thought better than the Jordan? .... ☐

4. In what river were the hosts of Sisera swept away? .... ☐

5. Near what river did Jacob wrestle with an angel? .... ☐

6. Beside what river did David fight Goliath? .... ☐

7. Name the lost rivers which bounded Eden. .... ☐

8. In what river was the baby Moses found? .... ☐

9. By what river were the Ten Tribes settled when carried into captivity? .... ☐

10. Which river is of greatest interest to Christians? .... ☐

Total score .... ☐

1. **Jordan** (Matt. 3:13); 2. **River of Egypt** (not the Nile) and the **Euphrates** (Gen. 15:18); 3. **Abana** and **Pharpar** (2 Kings 5:12); 4. **Kishon** (Judg. 5:21); 5. **Jabbok** (Gen. 32:22, 24); 6. **Elah** (2 Sam. 17:19); 7. **Pishon** and **Gihon** (Gen. 2:11); 8. **Nile** (Ex. 2:36); 9. **Habor** (2 Kings 17:6); 10. **The River of the Water of Life** (Rev. 22:1, 2).

BIBLE RIVERS—No. 2

1. Across which river of Canaan did the people of God walk when the waters were parted? .... ☐

2. What were the two large rivers of Mesopotamia? .... ☐

3. What river flows past Jerusalem? .... ☐

4. In what river did John baptize? .... ☐

5. What river did Moses turn to blood? .... ☐

6. Which river is called "the great river"? .... ☐

7. Elijah smote which river and the waters parted? ...... ☐

8. On what river is Nineveh located? .... ☐

9. Which river flows past Antioch? .... ☐

10. What "rivers of Damascus" vanish in the desert? ...... ☐

Total score .... ☐

1. **Jordan** (Josh. 3:15); 2. **Tigris** and **Euphrates**; 3. **Kidron**; 4. **Jordan** (Mark 1:5); 5. **Nile** (Ex. 8:20); 6. **Euphrates** (Gen. 15:18); 7. **Jordan** (2 Kings 2:8); 8. **Tigris**; 9. **Orontes**; 10. **Abana** and **Pharpar**.

BIBLE TREES

Count ten points for each correct answer.

1. Up what kind of tree did Zacchæus climb? .... ☐

2. Behind what kind of trees did the troops of David hide? .... ☐

3. What tree was a disappointment to Jesus? .... ☐

4. What kind of trees did Hiram send to Jerusalem? ...... ☐

5. In what kind of tree did Absalom catch his head? ...... ☐

6. What tree was first asked to be king, in Jotham's fable? .... ☐

7. What kind of trees did Solomon import to Jerusalem? ☐

8. What kind of tree was Jericho noted for? .... ☐

9. Under what kind of tree did Elijah sit? .... ☐

10. On what kind of trees did the captive Jews hang their harps? .... ☐

Total score .... ☐

1. **Sycamore** (Luke 19:1-4); 2. **Mulberry** (2 Sam. 5:22-24); 3. **Fig** (Mark 11:13); 4. **Cedar** (1 Kings 5:1-6); 5. **Oak** (2 Sam. 18:9); 6. **Olive** (Judg. 9:8); 7. **Algum** (2 Chron. 9:10, 11); 8. **Palm** (Deut. 34:3); 9. **Juniper** (1 Kings 19:4); 10. **Willows** (Ps. 137:1-4).

BOOKS OF THE BIBLE

1. **Which was the first book written?**

   Job. (Job is believed to have been a contemporary of Abraham. He lived in the land of Uz, which was so-called at that time; he was the priest of the family and offered up sacrifices, a practice which preceded the Law; he lived to a great age.)

2. **Which was the last book written?**

   Revelation.

3. **Which is the longest book?**

   Psalms.

4. **Which was written by a general?**

   Joshua.

5. **Which was written by a scribe?**

   Ezra.

6. **Which were written by a lawgiver?**

   The first five Old Testament books were written by Moses.

7. **Which books were written by a "wise man"?**

   Proverbs, Ecclesiastes, Song of Solomon.

8. **Which books were written by a "weeping prophet"?**

   Jeremiah, Lamentations.

9. **Which book was written by a man who was a cupbearer to a king?**

   Nehemiah.

10. **Which book was written by a herdsman?**

    Amos.

11. **Which book was written by a man whose wife deserted him?**

    Hosea.

17

12. **Which books were written by kings?**
    David and Solomon wrote Psalms, Proverbs, Ecclesiastes and Song of Solomon.

13. **Which book was written by a taxgatherer?**
    Matthew.

14. **Which books were written by brothers of Jesus?**
    James and Jude.

15. **Which apostle wrote the most books?**
    Paul.

16. **Which book was written about a runaway slave?**
    Philemon.

17. **Which books were written by a physician?**
    Luke and Acts.

18. **Which book tells stories of the beginning of things?**
    Genesis.

19. **Which book tells stories about the end of things?**
    Revelation.

20. **Which books tell about the life of Jesus?**
    Matthew, Mark, Luke and John.

21. **Which book tells the story of the founding of the church?**
    Acts.

22. **Which books have only one chapter?**
    Obadiah, Philemon, 2 John, 3 John, Jude.

23. **Which book was written about a queen?**
    Esther.

24. **Which books were written about women?**
    Ruth and Esther.

25. **Which book tells what to do to be saved?**
    The Book of Acts.

NEW TESTAMENT BOOKS

1. **Which Gospel was written primarily for the Jews?**
   Matthew.

2. **Which Gospel was written primarily for the Gentiles?**
   Luke.

3. **Which Gospel was written primarily for the Romans?**
   Mark.

4. **Which book is called "Paul's Gospel"?**
   Romans.

5. **Which Gospel writers were numbered among the "twelve"?**
   Matthew and John.

6. **Which book deals with "justification by faith"?**
   Romans.

7. **Which book deals with "works" as necessary to salvation?**
   James.

8. **Which book was written because some were beginning to preach "another gospel"?**
   Galatians.

9. **Which Gospel writer wrote a second book continuing his story?**
   Luke.

10. **Which book deals with divisions in the church?**
    1 Corinthians.

11. **Which letter was probably a "circular" letter?**

    Ephesians.

12. **Which Epistle is the most joyous one?**

    Philippians.

13. **Which Epistle did Luther call "an epistle of straw"?**

    James.

14. **Which book was written to correct a false notion about the resurrection?**

    2 Thessalonians.

15. **Which was the last book written by Paul?**

    2 Timothy (4:6).

16. **Which book was addressed to a slave-owner of Colosse?**

    Philemon.

17. **Which book gives a definition of "pure religion"?**

    James (1:27).

18. **Which books were written to encourage people in a time of persecution?**

    1 Peter and Revelation.

19. **Which book is addressed to "the elect lady"?**

    2 John.

20. **Which book tells the story of the end of the world?**

    Revelation.

OLD TESTAMENT NAMES

With what word do you associate each particular name?

ADAM ....temple, **garden,** palace.

EVE ....**serpent,** lion, lamb.

NOAH ....lightning, earthquake, **rainbow.**

ABRAHAM ....Babylon, **Ur,** Damascus.

ISAAC ....Rachel, Leah, **Rebekah.**

JACOB ....generous, **deceiver,** patriot.

ESAU ....covenant, **birthright,** testament.

JOSEPH ....revenge, **forgiveness,** pride.

MOSES ....**law,** prophets, gospel.

AARON ....**priest,** publican, scribe.

JOSHUA ....lawyer, **soldier,** king.

EHUD ....one-armed, **left-handed,** deaf.

DEBORAH ....priestess, **judge,** deaconess.

GIDEON ....**trumpets,** cymbals, drums.

SAMSON ....wolf, **lion,** bear.

RUTH ....spinner, **gleaner,** weaver.

SAUL ....**big man,** good man, stingy man.

DAVID ....cattle, **sheep,** goats.

ABSALOM ....loyal, **rebellious,** kind.

JONATHAN ....stewardship, **friendship,** leadership.

SOLOMON ....magic, music, **wisdom.**

REHOBOAM ....**pride,** humility, sincerity.

HEZEKIAH ....**trust,** fear, indifference.

AHAB ....good, **evil,** ignorant.

JEZEBEL ....clothing, **cosmetics,** jewelry.

ESTHER ....**self-sacrifice,** generosity, disdain.

DANIEL ....signature, **handwriting,** legacy.

ELIJAH ....caravan, **chariot,** wagon.

JONAH ....Babylon, **Nineveh,** Tarsus.

ATHALIAH ....honor, loyalty, **treason.**

21

NEW TESTAMENT NAMES

With what word do you associate each particular name?

HEROD ....**cruel,** kind, haughty.

NICODEMUS ....day, twilight, **night.**

ZACCHÆUS ....**tall, short,** fat.

JOHN ....**bold,** fearful, compromising.

LUKE ....**gospel,** epistle, revelation.

MATTHEW ....**publican,** sinner, priest.

THOMAS ....faith, **doubt,** credulity.

ANDREW ....taxgatherer, **fisherman,** shepherd.

JAMES ....Matthew, Mark, **John.**

CAIAPHAS ....prophet, lawyer, **priest.**

MARTHA ....fashions, parties, **dinners.**

JUDAS ....Bethel, **Kerioth,** Gerasa.

PILATE ....courage, **compromise,** fear.

MATTHIAS ....judges, prophets, **apostles.**

ANANIAS ....witnessing, **lying,** testifying.

GAMALIEL ....**lawyer,** doctor, scribe.

STEPHEN ....**martyr,** renegade, proselyte.

PHILIP ....**evangelist,** elder, prophet.

APOLLOS ....deacon, **orator,** silversmith.

TIMOTHY ....Barnabas, **Paul,** Peter.

LUKE ....tentmaker, **physician,** fisherman.

PAUL ....Alexandria, Nazareth, **Tarsus.**

BARABBAS ....the Exodus, captivity, **crucifixion.**

GABRIEL ....high priest, **angel,** Levite.

CLUES

In seeking to identify these characters, read the clues slowly to the contestant, and have him tell the name as quickly as possible. If sides are chosen, allow a point for the number of clues needed to determine the name; that is, if the contestant gets the name on the fourth clue, that will be four points, or on the second clue, two points. The side having the fewest points will win.

(1)

1. This man was a Levite.
2. He was a mouthpiece for Moses.
3. He was the first high priest.
4. His mother's name was Jochebed.
5. He made a golden calf.

Aaron

(2)

1. This young man was handsome.
2. He won the hearts of the people.
3. He rebelled against his father.
4. He caught his hair in a tree, and was killed by his enemies.
5. He was a son of David.

Absalom

(3)

1. This man lived during the Exodus.
2. He caused Israel to be defeated at Ai.
3. He stole money and garments at Jericho.
4. He was brought to trial and confessed.
5. He was stoned to death.

Achan

23

(4)

1. This man was a priest of the most high God.
2. He was king of Salem.
3. He met Abraham after he had rescued Lot.
4. He received tithes from Abraham.
5. He was a type of Christ.

Melchizedek

(5)

1. This man was the first Hebrew.
2. He dwelt in the city of Hebron.
3. He bought the cave of Machpelah.
4. God made a covenant with him.
5. He married his half-sister.

Abraham

(6)

1. This man was a herdsman.
2. He said he was "no prophet or son of a prophet."
3. But God called him to be a prophet.
4. He lived in the city of Tekoa.
5. He wrote a book of the Bible.

Amos

(7)

1. This man lived in Damascus.
2. He was a true Christian.
3. He was told to go to Saul.
4. He was afraid to visit him.
5. He restored Saul's sight and baptized him.

Ananias

1. He was a good son of a bad father.
2. He became king as a boy.
3. He caused the temple to be repaired.
4. The book of the law was found.
5. He was killed in a battle with Pharaoh-necho.

Josiah

(9)

1. This girl was an Egyptian.
2. She was daughter of the priest of On.
3. She married a man who ranked next to Pharaoh.
4. She had two children, Ephraim and Manasseh.
5. She was the wife of Joseph.

Asenath

(10)

1. This girl was also an Egyptian.
2. She was a slave girl.
3. She became a wife of Abraham.
4. She was the mother of Ishmael.
5. She was a source of trouble in the family.

Hagar

(11)

1. This woman was a daughter of Amram.
2. She was very clever when a girl.
3. She objected to Moses' wife.
4. She was smitten temporarily with leprosy.
5. She wrote a song.

Miriam

1. This woman was a judge.
2. She was also a prophetess.
3. Her court was held under a palm tree.
4. She accompanied Barak when he led his army against Sisera.
5. She wrote a song of victory.

Deborah

(13)

1. This man was also one of the judges.
2. He was threshing wheat when an angel appeared.
3. He was called to be a leader of Israel.
4. He was afraid because his family was the poorest in Manasseh.
5. He won a victory without striking a blow.

Gideon

(14)

1. This man was a prophet of God.
2. At one time he thought he was the only one left who worshiped Jehovah.
3. A wicked queen sought his life.
4. He sat under a juniper tree, and asked to die.
5. He was taken up to heaven in a whirlwind.

Elijah

(15)

1. He was a brother-in-law of Moses.
2. He was a Midianite.
3. He was asked to guide Israel through the wilderness.
4. He refused to be hired.
5. He volunteered to go.

Hobab

1. He was a tentmaker.
2. He had been banished from Rome.
3. He met Paul in Corinth.
4. He went with Paul to Ephesus.
5. He taught Apollos the way of the Lord more perfectly.

Aquila

1. He was a Greek.
2. He was one of Paul's helpers.
3. He went to Jerusalem with Paul.
4. He was left in charge of the work in Crete.
5. Paul wrote an Epistle to him.

Titus

1. He was a high priest and a judge.
2. His sons were wicked men.
3. He had a boy-assistant in the tabernacle.
4. The boy brought him a message from God.
5. He died when he heard the ark was captured in battle.

Eli

1. He was returning home from Jerusalem.
2. He was reading the Book of Isaiah.
3. Philip joined him in the chariot.
4. Philip converted and baptized him.
5. He went on his way rejoicing.

Ethiopian

1. He was an Aramean, or Syrian.
2. He was a cheater.
3. He sold two daughters to one man.
4. He was an idolater.
5. He made a covenant with Jacob at Mizpah.

Laban

(21)

1. He took advantage of his uncle.
2. He moved to a wicked city.
3. He was elected to a city office.
4. He was warned by angels to leave.
5. His wife was turned to a pillar of salt.

Lot

(22)

1. He lived in Colosse.
2. He was converted by Paul.
3. The church met in his house.
4. He had a slave who ran away.
5. Paul wrote him a letter.

Philemon

(23)

1. He was one of Jesus' disciples.
2. He had a big voice.
3. He was Jesus' best friend.
4. He saw a vision of heaven.
5. He was the last apostle to die.

John

1. He was half-Greek, half-Jew.
2. He lived in Lystra.
3. He had a godly mother.
4. He was Paul's right-hand man.
5. Paul wrote two letters to him.

Timothy

1. He was one of the "twelve."
2. He lived in Capernaum.
3. He was the first apostle to be killed.
4. He wanted to sit at the right hand of Jesus.
5. His father's name was Zebedee.

James

FATHERS AND SONS

Match the fathers and sons.

1.	Adam	Manasseh	9.	Kish	Moses
2.	Noah	Solomon	10.	Saul	Ephraim
3.	Abraham	Rehoboam	11.	Jesse	Judah
4.	Isaac	Noah	12.	David	Esau
5.	Jacob	David	13.	Lamech	Isaac
6.	Joseph	Jonathan	14.	Hezekiah	Shem
7.	Amram	Saul	15.	Solomon	Seth
8.	Nun	Joshua			

Answers

1.	Adam	Seth	9.	Kish	Saul
2.	Noah	Shem	10.	Saul	Jonathan
3.	Abraham	Isaac	11.	Jesse	David
4.	Isaac	Esau	12.	David	Solomon
5.	Jacob	Judah	13.	Lamech	Noah
6.	Joseph	Ephraim	14.	Hezekiah	Manasseh
7.	Amram	Moses	15.	Solomon	Rehoboam
8.	Nun	Joshua			

MOTHERS AND SONS

Match the mothers and sons.

1.	Eve	Timothy	9.	Mary	Jacob
2.	Sarah	Obed	10.	Elisabeth	Benjamin
3.	Hagar	Judah	11.	Eunice	Ephraim
4.	Rebekah	Mahlon	12.	Ruth	Moses
5.	Rachel	Ahaziah	13.	Leah	Samuel
6.	Asenath	Abel	14.	Naomi	Jesus
7.	Jochebed	Isaac	15.	Jezebel	John
8.	Hanna	Ishmael			

Answers

1. Eve ....Abel
2. Sarah ....Isaac
3. Hagar ....Ishmael
4. Rebekah ....Jacob
5. Rachel ....Benjamin
6. Asenath ....Ephraim
7. Jochebed ....Moses
8. Hannah ....Samuel

9. Mary ....Jesus
10. Elisabeth ....John
11. Eunice ....Timothy
12. Ruth ....Obed
13. Leah ....Judah
14. Naomi ....Mahlon
15. Jezebel ....Ahaziah

HUSBANDS AND WIVES

Match the husbands and wives.

1. Adam ....Sapphira
2. Abraham ....Priscilla
3. Ahab ....Esther
4. Ananias ....Ruth
5. Aquila ....Rebekah
6. Ahasuerus ....Jezebel
7. David ....Eve
8. Boaz ....Rachel

9. Isaac ....Sarah
10. Jacob ....Michal
11. Joseph ....Asenath
12. Jehoram ....Bernice
13. Agrippa ....Elisabeth
14. Zacharias ....Athaliah
15. Elkanah ....Hannah

Answers

1. Adam ....Eve
2. Abraham ....Sarah
3. Ahab ....Jezebel
4. Ananias ....Sapphira
5. Aquila ....Priscilla
6. Ahasuerus ....Esther
7. David ....Michal
8. Boaz ....Ruth

9. Isaac ....Rebekah
10. Jacob ....Rachel
11. Joseph ....Asenath
12. Jehoram ....Athaliah
13. Agrippa ....Bernice
14. Zacharias ....Elisabeth
15. Elkanah ....Hannah

PERSONS AND EVENTS

Match the persons and events.

1. Moses ....Became prime minister of Egypt.
2. Cain ....Fought with a giant.
3. Noah ....Became first high priest.
4. Jacob ....Chosen first king of Israel.
5. Joshua ....Had the answer to every question.
6. Aaron ....Caused the Red Sea to part.
7. Methuselah ....Took the longest boat ride.
8. Joseph ....Wrestled with an angel.
9. David ....Fed by the ravens.
10. Saul ....Took the first submarine trip.
11. Solomon ....Climbed a tree to see Jesus.
12. Elijah ....Commanded the sun to stand still.
13. Jonah ....Lived the longest of all men.
14. Peter ....Slew his brother.
15. Zacchæus ....Saw a vision on the housetop.

Answers

1. Moses ....Caused the Red Sea to part.
2. Cain ....Slew his brother.
3. Noah ....Took the longest boat ride.
4. Jacob ....Wrestled with an angel.
5. Joshua ....Commanded the sun to stand still.
6. Aaron ....Became first high priest.
7. Methuselah ....Lived the longest of all men.
8. Joseph ....Became prime minister of Egypt.
9. David ....Fought with a giant.
10. Saul ....Chosen first king of Israel.
11. Solomon ....Had the answer to every question.
12. Elijah ....Fed by the ravens.
13. Jonah ....Took the first submarine trip.
14. Peter ....Saw a vision on the housetop.
15. Zacchæus ....Climbed a tree to see Jesus.

I needed a gardener, so I accosted an old darky sitting under a tree idly watching the sea gulls flying over the bay.

"Do you want a **job,** or are you wor**king s**omewhere?" I asked.

"Nassuh," he answered, "Ah ain't got no job jes' now; Ah'm taking' a vacation, yo' see."

"Got a family to support?" I inquired.

"Yassuh, a wife an' six chilluns," he replied.

"Well, don't you know the Bible says that if a man will not work, he shall not eat? Haven't you got any religion?"

"Yassuh, Ah done got 'li**jon Ah** knows, an Ah keers fer mah family."

"Where did you work last?"

"On de good shi**p 'Rover B,' s**o Ah did. We brought in shrimps by de bushel."

"Why did you qui**t it? U**sually people don't quit working unless there is a reason."

"Mah hands kept gettin' **numb er s**ore; Ah had to keep them shrimp iced."

"Nonsense. That ought to have been a pleasant task on a hot day. You just didn't want to work, isn't that it?"

"Nassuh, Ah had **a mos'** pleasant time on that ship," he replied.

"And where do your meals come from now?"

"Oh, de Lawd, he pervide. To**o bad I a h**eavy eater, though."

"Yoo-hoo, pappy!" cried a voice down the way.

"Heah Ah is, Oleander," he answered.

"Is that your child?" I asked.

"Yassuh, dat's my gal at I answered. She just at de age when she try to mimic a hyena, but she smart all right. She knows a dog is an animal, a chicken is a fowl."

"Where do you live from here?"

"In a humble little shack down de beach. Ah likes to sit beside it and make music in de moonlight. Ah plays de ban jo elegantly, and mah wife plays de guitar. Oh, man, such music as we do make."

"Come, now, why don't you face the facts and do something to take care of your family beside making music? Do you want that job as gardener, or don't you?"

"Nassuh, Ah done told de cap'n of the 'Rover B' I would start again tomorrow."

(In this little story are fifteen names of Bible books. These should be underscored, when found, if the story is used in a contest at a party.)

34

FIND THE HIDDEN CITIES

Sheik **Ek Ron**gil was in a predicament. Arriving at the oasis in midafternoon, after having been away for several weeks, he found a messenger waiting to announce that an old friend, **Emile Tus**ka would arrive that very day to visit him, and, since the sun was already beginning to get low in the west, he might arrive at any moment. It was an embarrassing situation. No honored guest had ever visited him without much preparation being made for his entertainment, and now the time was at hand.

The Sheik groaned. Provisions were low. "My friend, Tuska, will expect a feast such as **Cæsar ea**ts, and in all my camp there is nothing better than the poor fare of a fellahin. I might send and **ask Elon** Abdul to come to my assistance. But no, that is too far. Even my swiftest camels could not get back by nightfall. The matter really is **ur**gent. If I serve him only goat's milk and cheese, he will think we are still living back in **the bron**ze age."

Quickly he went to Ar**beth, el**derly aunt of his wife, who had been doing the cooking on the journey and told his plight. She laughed at his bewilderment, for the Sheik took pride in coolheadedness, even in the face of robber bullets. "A glorious host will the Sheik make tonight," said she. "A servant of servants I would rather **be than y**ou. Indeed, it is little more than a servant I am in your camp, though I may be called tutor to your children. Your wife can not cook, but if she will keep the **baby lon**g enough, I will see what can be done."

A survey of the remaining food was made, but it was disheartening. Only by skimping would they have enough to enable them to reach their home at El **Gath**ra. There sprang up ran**cor in th**e heart of the Sheik. He was anxious to see his old friend, but why, after all these years, did their trails

35

have to cross at a time like this? How had he offended Allah, that this should be?

A cloud of dust appeared on the desert trail. The time had come. It was kismet! With heavy heart, Sheik Ek Ron-**gil gal**loped out to meet the coming guest. But lo, this was no camel train! It was a commissary caravan from Damascus! Allah be praised! There would now be food, and to spare!

The caravan proved to be a string of American trucks operating between **Damascus** and **Petra,** and owned by a concern in **Philadelphia,** and they crossed the wastelands of Arabia in double-quick time, at about so many miles **per ga**llon.

Quickly, the Sheik ordered provisions, and preparations were made for the evening meal. As the sun was sinking, his old friend appeared, and he was welcomed with profuse oriental hospitality.

As they sat about the delicious banquet that evening, Emile Tuska said, "You have no idea how wonderful that **roas**t lamb tastes, and that **fat hen s**urely is grand. You see, **from e**arly morn until now, we have tasted nothing. Our provisions ran out last night, and we might nigh have starved before getting home. Your hospitality is appreciated beyond words. I certainly **do than**k you."

"Think nothing of it, my friend," said Ek Rongil. "It is kismet!"

(In this story are the names of twenty Bible cities. These are to be underscored when found, as shown above. Philadelphia, though an American city, was also the name of a city in Asia Minor.)

FIND THE OCCUPATION

1. Elijah		1.	Fisherman
2. Pilate		2.	Taxgatherer
3. Moses		3.	Physician
4. Paul		4.	Lawgiver
5. John		5.	Scribe
6. Lazarus		6.	King
7. Matthew		7.	Prophet
8. Ezra		8.	Silversmith
9. Luke		9.	Tentmaker
10. Hezekiah		10.	Governor
11. Demetrius		11.	Beggar
12. Gamaliel		12.	Centurion
13. Amos		13.	Deacon
14. Onesimus		14.	Sorcerer
15. Zacchæus		15.	Steward
16. Cornelius		16.	General
17. Cain		17.	Herdsman
18. Aaron		18.	Lawyer
19. Eliezer		19.	Publican
20. Simon Magus		20.	Judge
21. Nehemiah		21.	Cupbearer
22. Philip		22.	Slave
23. Sennacherib		23.	Farmer
24. Eli		24.	High priest

1	7	7	2	13	17	19	15
2	10	8	5	14	22	20	14
3	4	9	3	15	19	21	21
4	9	10	6	16	12	22	13
5	1	11	8	17	23	23	16
6	11	12	18	18	24	24	20

FIND THE PLACE—No. 1

1. The birth of Jesus was at what city? .... 1. Cæsarea
2. Where did the death of Moses take place? .... 2. Gath
3. Where did Abram locate in Palestine? .... 3. Jericho
4. Find the home of a witch. .... 4. Dothan
5. Where did the ark rest at the close of the flood? .... 5. Damascus
6. Where was the temple located? .... 6. Kerioth
7. Where did Saul meet his death? .... 7. Bethlehem
8. Where was the law given? .... 8. Endor
9. Where did Jesus have His headquarters? .... 9. Gilboa
10. Where did Moses take his first boat ride? ....10. Nebo
11. What was the Roman capital of Palestine? ....11. Capernaum
12. Where were the "wells of Abraham"? ....12. Nile
13. Where did Jesus live as a boy? ....13. Bethshean
14. Where did the "good confession" take place? ....14. Hebron
15. What was the home of Mary and Martha? ....15. Ararat
16. Where was the home of Goliath? ......16. Elah
17. Where was the tabernacle located?....17. Beersheba
18. Where did "Simon, the tanner" live? ....18. Jerusalem
19. The walls of what city fell down? ......19. Sinai
20. Where did Joseph find his brothers and the sheep? ....20. Nazareth

21. What is the capital of Syria? ....21. Cæsarea Philippi
22. Where was the home of Judas? ....22. Bethany
23. On the walls of what city did the
      Philistines hang the body of
      Saul? ....23. Shiloh
24. Where did David fight Goliath? ....24. Joppa
25. Where was the home of Philip? ....25. Bethsaida

1 7	10 12	19 3
2 10	11 1	20 4
3 14	12 17	21 5
4 8	13 20	22 6
5 15	14 21	23 13
6 18	15 22	24 16
7 9	16 2	25 25
8 19	17 23	
9 11	18 24	

FIND THE PLACE—No. 2

1. Paul had a vision on the way to what
    city? .... 1. Ephesus
2. In what city did Belshazzer see the
    "handwriting on the wall"? .... 2. Tarsus
3. Where did Moses raise the "brazen
    serpent"? .... 3. Jerusalem
4. Which was "the city of palm trees"? .... 4. Damascus
5. Where did Jeroboam place two golden
    calves? .... 5. Babylon
6. Where did Aaron make a golden calf?.... 6. Wilderness
7. Where did Elijah contest the priests
    of Baal? .... 7. Jericho
8. Where was the first miracle of Jesus
    performed? .... 8. Dan, Bethel
9. Where was Paul's birthplace? .... 9. Mt. Carmel

10. Where was the riot of the silversmiths?....10. Sinai
11. Where is the pool of Siloam located? ......11. Cana
12. Where did Jacob have a vision of
    angels? ....12. Sychar
13. Where was Jesus' first home? ....13. Samaria
14. In what land did Esther live? ....14. Moab
15. In what land did Ruth live? ....15. Bethel
16. Where was Jacob's well located? ....16. Egypt
17. Where did Ahab have his ivory palace?....17. Persia
18. What city was called "the city of
    David"? ....18. Red Sea
19. What was Abram's native city? ....19. Sea of Galilee
20. What sea did the Israelites cross? ....20. Bethlehem
21. On what water did Jesus walk? ....21. Ur
22. Of what country was Goliath a native?....22. Antioch
23. Where did Paul go first on his first
    missionary journey? ....23. Philistia
24. Where were the disciples first called
    "Christians"? ....24. Lystra
25. Where was Paul stoned and left for
    dead? ....25. Cyprus

1	4	10	1	19	21
2	5	11	3	20	18
3	6	12	15	21	19
4	7	13	16	22	23
5	8	14	17	23	25
6	10	15	14	24	22
7	9	16	12	25	24
8	11	17	13		
9	2	18	20		

WHO IS IT?

1. A man whose eyes were not dim at the age of 120 years?
   Moses (Deut. 34:7).

2. A man who called himself "a dead dog"?
   Mephibosheth (2 Sam. 9:8).

3. A man on Mt. Carmel having a contest with the priests of Baal?
   Elijah (1 Kings 18:20-40).

4. A maid gleaning in the field of Boaz?
   Ruth (Ruth 2:5-7).

5. An aged man who crossed his hands when blessing his grandchildren?
   Jacob (Gen. 48:13-19).

6. A man who was told to take the shoes from off his feet, for he was standing on holy ground?
   Moses (Ex. 3:8).

7. A young man who was sleeping with a stone for a pillow?
   Jacob (Gen. 28:11).

8. A young man who was known as a foot racer?
   Asahel (2 Sam. 2:18).

9. A ruler to whom Jesus refused to speak?
   Herod (Luke 23:8).

10. A captain who was told to wash in the Jordan River?
    Naaman (2 Kings 5:10).

11. A young man thrown into a lions' den?
    Daniel (Dan. 6:16).

12. **A king who saw handwriting on the palace wall?**
    Belshazzar (Dan. 5:5).

13. **A boy who saw his parents and brothers bow down before him in a dream?**
    Joseph (Gen. 37:5-11).

14. **A man who was liberated from prison by an angel?**
    Peter (Acts 12:7-19).

15. **A boy who heard the voice of God?**
    Samuel (1 Sam. 3:1-9).

16. **A king who hurled a spear at a boy?**
    Saul (1 Sam. 18:11).

17. **A prophet who had a dream of a ram and a billy-goat?**
    Daniel (Dan. 8:1-8).

18. **A governor's wife who had a bad dream?**
    Pilate's wife (Matt. 27:19).

19. **An aged prophetess who blessed the baby Jesus?**
    Anna (Luke 2:36-38).

20. **A king who was smitten as the people cried out that he had the voice of a god?**
    Herod (Acts 12:22, 23).

21. **A woman who anointed Jesus with costly perfume?**
    Mary of Bethany (John 12:3).

22. **A king who dreamed of a tree?**
    Nebuchadnezzar (Dan. 4:10-27).

23. **The people who thought Paul and Barnabas were gods?**
    The Lycaonians (Acts 14:8-18).

24. **A woman who made garments for the needy?**
    Dorcas (Acts 9:39).

25. **A good man who asked Pilate for the body of Jesus?**
   Joseph of Arimathea (John 19:38).

26. **A prophet who caused a great drought in Israel?**
   Elijah (1 Kings 17:1).

27. **A man who was a king's cupbearer?**
   Nehemiah (Neh. 1:11).

28. **A queen who said, "If I perish, I perish"?**
   Esther (Esth. 4:16).

29. **A prophet who was taken to heaven in a whirlwind?**
   Elijah (2 Kings 2:11).

30. **A soldier who was a fast driver?**
   Jehu (2 Kings 9:20).

31. **Three boys who were cast into a fiery furnace?**
   Shadrach, Meshach and Abednego (Dan. 3:20).

32. **A king who had an ivory throne?**
   Solomon (1 Kings 10:18).

33. **A man who broke two tables of stone?**
   Moses (Ex. 32:19).

34. **A woman who turned to a pillar of salt?**
   Lot's wife (Gen. 19:26).

35. **A man whose wages were changed ten times?**
   Jacob (Gen. 31:41).

36. **A man who wrestled with an angel?**
   Jacob (Gen. 32:26).

37. **A man who was buried by the Lord?**
   Moses (Deut. 34:6).

38. **A man who commanded the sun to stand still?**
   Joshua (Josh. 10:12).

39. **A man who made a golden calf?**
     Aaron (Ex. 32:1-6).

40. **A man who made two golden calves?**
     Jeroboam (1 Kings 12:28).

41. **A man who didn't want to be his "brother's keeper"?**
     Cain (Gen. 4:9).

42. **A boy who wore a coat of many colors?**
     Joseph (Gen. 37:23).

43. **A man who saw a burning bush?**
     Moses (Ex. 3:1-5).

44. **A man who sold his birthright for a mess of pottage?**
     Esau (Gen. 25:34).

45. **A baby placed in an ark of bulrushes?**
     Moses (Ex. 2:3).

46. **A great man whose grave was unknown?**
     Moses (Deut. 34:6).

47. **A woman who was called "the mother of all living"?**
     Eve (Gen. 3:20).

48. **A king who took away the gold shields from the temple?**
     Shishak (1 Kings 14:26).

49. **A king who removed his wicked mother from being queen?**
     Asa (1 Kings 15:13).

50. **A prophet who was fed by the ravens?**
     Elijah (1 Kings 17:6).

CONCERNING JERUSALEM

1. **What is the earliest name of Jerusalem mentioned in the Bible?**
   Salem (Gen. 14:18).

2. **What was the city called when the Israelites came back from Egypt?**
   Jebus (Josh. 18:28. The people were called Jebusites.)

3. **What is the city often called?**
   The Holy City (Neh. 11:1); Zion (1 Kings 8:1); City of the Great King (Ps. 48:2).

4. **Is Jerusalem on the hills or in the valley?**
   It is built on four hills in the Central Range. The altitude is about 2,593 feet.

5. **Who first captured this city?**
   David's men (1 Chron. 11:4-9).

6. **Who brought the ark of the covenant to Jerusalem?**
   David (2 Sam. 6:1-15).

7. **Who built the temple in Jerusalem?**
   Solomon (1 Kings 6:1).

8. **When was the temple destroyed?**
   586 B. C., by the soldiers of Nebuchadnezzar.

9. **Who rebuilt the temple?**
   Zerubbabel (Ezra 3:2).

10. **What king plundered Jerusalem, and took money from the temple treasury?**
    Shishak (1 Kings 14:25, 26).

11. **Who is the first king mentioned in connection with Jerusalem?**
    Melchizedek (Gen. 14:18).

12. **What river runs past Jerusalem?**
    The Kidron (2 Sam. 15:23).

13. **What valley runs west and south of the city?**
    Hinnom (Josh. 15:8).

14. **What famous pool was in Jerusalem?**
    The Pool of Siloam (John 9:7).

15. **What army met disaster in a strange way outside the city walls?**
    The Assyrians under Sennacherib (2 Kings 19:35).

16. **Who burned Jerusalem and laid it waste?**
    Nebuchadnezzar (2 Kings 25:9, 10).

17. **Was Jesus born in Jerusalem?**
    No. Bethlehem (Matt. 2:1).

18. **Who was in control of Jerusalem during the time of Jesus?**
    The Romans.

19. **Who was the Roman governor?**
    Pilate (John 18:29).

20. **Did Jesus spend most of His time in Jerusalem?**
    No; only when He attended the feasts. Jesus spent most of His time in Galilee.

21. **What prophecy did Jesus make concerning the temple?**
    That not one stone would be left upon another (Luke 19:42-44).

22. **When did this come to pass?**
    A. D. 70, when the Romans destroyed the city.

23. **Was Jesus crucified in Jerusalem?**
    No. It was outside the city at Calvary, or Golgotha (Luke 23:33; Matt. 27:33).

24. **What event took place fifty days after the resurrection?**
    The founding of the church on Pentecost (Acts 1:4; 2:1-4, 41-47).

KIND DEEDS

1. Who was the uncle who gave his nephew the choice of the land for his flocks, and he chose the Jordan Valley?
   Abraham.

2. Who was the man who forgave his brothers when they had sold him as a slave?
   Joseph.

3. Who was the sister who looked after her little brother when he was placed in an ark in the bulrushes?
   Miriam.

4. Who was the boy who could have taken Saul's life in a cave when Saul was seeking to kill him?
   David.

5. Who was the friend who saved David's life by shooting arrows to signal him?
   Jonathan.

6. Who was the queen who risked her life to save her people?
   Esther.

7. Who was the king who let a crippled prince, Mephibosheth, eat regularly at his table, though a son of his enemy?
   David.

8. Who was the man who left a job in the king's palace to go back to Jerusalem and help rebuild the city?
   Nehemiah.

9. What men came a long distance to see the boy Jesus?
   The Wise-men.

10. What kind person helped a man who had been injured by robbers?
    The good Samaritan.

11. Who was the Man who fed a multitude of people who had nothing to eat?

Jesus.

12. What man stayed close to Jesus when His other disciples forsook Him?

John.

13. What kind man looked after the mother of Jesus when He was being crucified?

John.

14. What woman brought sweet perfume to anoint Jesus?

Mary.

15. Who were the women who invited Jesus to dinner frequently?

Mary and Martha.

16. What prophet brought back to life a widow's son?

Elisha.

17. What kind man healed a girl possessed of an evil spirit, who told fortunes?

Paul.

18. Who was the good doctor who stayed with Paul when he was imprisoned?

Luke.

19. What kind man received Paul when he came to Thessalonica?

Jason.

20. When Paul was temporarily blinded by his vision at Damascus, what man came and restored his sight?

Ananias.

21. **What boy helped Jesus perform a miracle?**
    The boy with the loaves and fishes.

22. **What boy became Paul's helper?**
    Timothy.

23. **What boy saved Paul's life by discovering a plot against him?**
    His nephew.

24. **What boy in a parable came back to his father's house?**
    The prodigal son.

25. **What boy got anointed king while out hunting his father's mules?**
    Saul.

FINISH THE SENTENCE

1. "Be ye doers of the word, —and not hearers only, deceiving your own selves" (Jas. 1:22).

2. "Even so faith, if it hath not works, —is dead, being alone" (Jas. 2:17).

3. "Be ye holy, —for I am holy" (1 Pet. 1:16b).

4. "If any man suffer as a Christian, —let him not be ashamed" (1 Pet. 4:16a).

5. "One day is with the Lord as a thousand years, —and a thousand years as one day" (2 Pet. 3:8b).

6. "The day of the Lord will come —as a thief in the night" (2 Pet. 3:10a).

7. "If we say that we have no sin, —we deceive ourselves, and the truth is not in us" (1 John 1:8).

8. "We love him, —because he first loved us" (John 4:19).

49

9. "Be thou faithful unto death, —and I will give thee a crown of life" (Rev. 2:10b).

10. "Blessed are the dead —which die in the Lord" (Rev. 14:13b).

11. "Greater love hath no man than this, —that a man lay down his life for his friends" (John 15:13).

12. "Righteousness exalteth a nation, —but sin is a reproach to any people" (Prov. 14:34).

13. "Train up a child in the way he should go: —and when he is old, he will not depart from it" (Prov. 22:6).

14. "A soft answer turneth away wrath: —but grievous words stir up anger" (Prov. 15:1).

15. "Where your treasure is, —there will your heart be also" (Matt. 6:21).

16. What therefore God hath joined together, —let no man put asunder" (Mark 10:9).

17. "Draw nigh to God, —and he will draw nigh to you" (Jas. 4:8).

18. "Judge not, —that ye be not judged" (Matt. 7:1a).

19. "All things work together for good —to them that love God" (Rom. 8:28a).

20. "We ought to obey God —rather than men" (Acts 5:29b).

21. "Blessed are the pure in heart: —for they shall see God" (Matt. 5:8).

22. "I am the way, —the truth, and the life" (John 14:6a).

23. "I am the vine, —ye are the branches" (John 15:5a).

24. "He that shall endure unto the end, —the same shall be saved" (Matt. 24:13).

25. "Heaven and earth shall pass away, —but my words shall not pass away" (Matt. 24: 35).

26. "If any man will come after me, —let him deny himself, and take up his cross, and follow me" (Matt. 16: 24).

27. "Whosoever will save his life shall lose it: —and whosoever will lose his life for my sake shall find it" (Matt. 16: 25).

28. "This people draweth nigh unto me with their mouth, and honoureth me with their lips, —but their heart is far from me" (Matt. 15: 8).

29. "But seek ye first the kingdom of God, and his righteousness, —and all these things shall be added unto you" (Matt. 6: 33).

30. "Strait is the gate, and narrow is the way, which leadeth unto life, —and few there be that find it" (Matt. 7: 14).

ANGELIC QUIZ

1. **What does the word "angel" mean?**
    It is from the Greek word, *angelos,* and it means "messenger."

2. **Are the angels superior to men?**
    Yes, while man is in his present state (Heb. 2: 7-9; 1 Cor. 6: 3).

3. **How many angels are there?**
    More than ten thousand times ten thousand (Rev. 5: 11).

4. **Are angels to be worshiped?**
    No (Rev. 19: 10; Col. 2: 18).

5. **Are angels married?**
    No (Matt. 22: 30).

6. **What is the fate of the angels that rebelled against God?**
   They are being held in "pits of darkness" until the
   time of judgment (2 Pet. 2:4; Jude 6).

7. **What man had a vision of angels ascending to and descending from heaven?**
   Jacob (Gen. 28:12).

8. **Do the angels sing?**
   Yes. They sang at the birth of Jesus (Luke 2:13-15;
   Rev. 5:8-13).

9. **What is the work of the angels?**
   They are servants of God (Ps. 103:21), and the servants of those who are Christians (Heb. 1:14).

10. **How did they serve Christ?**
    They strengthened Him at the time of temptation
    (Matt. 4:11). They were with Him in Gethsemane
    (Luke 22:43). They were attendants at the tomb and
    the ascension (Matt. 28:2-5; Acts 1:10). He could
    have had twelve legions of angels to come to His aid,
    had He desired it (Matt. 27:53).

11. **How have they served men?**
    They were attendants of the apostles (Acts 5:19;
    8:26; 12:7-11; 27:23, etc.).

12. **When were angels messengers of deliverance?**
    From the Midianites (Judg. 6:11-24). From the Assyrians (2 Kings 19:35); 2 Chron. 32:21). From
    Nebuchadnezzar (Dan. 3:28). From Herod (Matt.
    2:13, 19). From Jews (Acts 5:19; 12:7-11).

13. **What is the earliest task assigned to angels in the Bible?**
    Guarding the "tree of life" in Eden (Gen. 3:23).

14. **Is there any warrant for the term "guardian angels"?**
    A statement of Jesus would indicate that "little ones"
    have angels in heaven assigned to them (Matt. 18:10).

15. **Would it be wrong for us to ask the help of the angels?**

"Are they not all ministering spirits, sent forth to minister for them who shall be heirs of salvation?" (Heb. 1:14).

16. **Are the angels interested in us?**

"There is joy in the presence of the angels of God over one sinner that repenteth" (Luke 15:10).

17. **Do we know the names of any angels?**

Yes. Gabriel announced the birth of John and Jesus (Luke 1:19, 26). Michael is spoken of as a prince of angels (Dan. 12:1) and an archangel (Jude 9).

18. **Are angels capable of sinning?**

Yes (2 Pet. 2:4; Jude 6).

19. **Who are the fallen angels?**

Satan and his demons (Rev. 9:11; Luke 10:18).

20. **Do angels look like women?**

Angels always appeared in the form of men, and are always spoken of as "he" and "him." Since there is no marriage in heaven, it would appear that angels are neither men nor women, but sexless (Matt. 22:30).

SATANIC QUIZ

1. **How did Satan come to be the devil?**

By sinning (2 Pet. 2:4).

2. **What happened to the angels that rebelled against God?**

They were cast out of heaven (2 Pet. 2:4; Jude 6).

3. **Where is the place of their abode now?**

In pits of darkness (Greek—"Tartarus") (2 Pet. 2:4; Jude 6).

4. **By what names is Satan known?**

Adversary (1 Pet. 5:8); Apollyon (Rev. 9:11); Beelzebub (Matt. 12:24); Devil (Matt. 4:1); Prince of Demons (Matt. 2:24); Prince of the Powers of the Air (Eph. 2:2); Prince of This World (John 12:31); Tempter (Matt. 4:3; 1 Thess. 3:5).

5. **What kind of character is he?**

Liar and deceiver (John 8:44; 2 Thess. 2:9, 10); Murderer (John 8:44); Sinner (1 John 3:8); Tempter (Matt. 4:3); Destroys the Word (Matt. 13:37-40); Cunning (Eph. 6:11, 12); Enemy of righteousness (Acts 13:10); Hinders Christ's cause (Matt. 13:39).

6. **How may we overcome him?**

Watch and pray (Matt. 26:41); Resist (Eph. 4:27; Jas. 4:7); Put on the armor of God (Eph. 6:11).

7. **What will be his end?**

He is reserved for eternal fire (Matt. 25:41; Rev. 20:10).

8. **Was hell made for man?**

No, for the devil and his angels (Matt. 25:41).

9. **Who are those who will share the fate of the devil?**

The wicked (Matt. 25:41; Rev. 20:15).

10. **Is purgatory a sort of substation of hell?**

There is no such thing as purgatory taught in the Bible.

DREAM QUIZ

1. **What young man dreamed of a ladder reaching from earth to heaven?**

Jacob (Gen. 28:12).

2. **What boy is spoken of as "the dreamer"?**

Joseph (Gen. 37:14).

3. **Who dreamed of baskets of bread which were eaten by birds?**
   Pharaoh's baker (Gen. 40: 16-19).

4. **Who dreamed of a barley loaf?**
   A Midianite soldier (Judg. 7: 13).

5. **Who was offered the choice of anything he might ask in a dream?**
   Solomon (1 Kings 3: 5-15).

6. **Who had a dream of a great image?**
   Nebuchadnezzar (Dan. 2: 31-34).

7. **Who had a dream of seven fat cattle and seven lean cattle?**
   Pharaoh (Gen. 41: 17-21).

8. **Who dreamed of a ram and a he-goat?**
   Daniel (Dan. 8: 1-27).

9. **What governor's wife had a bad dream?**
   Pilate's wife (Matt. 27: 19).

10. **Who had a dream of four terrible beasts?**
    Daniel (Dan. 7: 2-8).

11. **Who dreamed of the sun, moon and stars doing obeisance to him?**
    Joseph (Gen. 37: 9).

12. **Who were warned in a dream not to return to Herod?**
    The Wise-men (Matt. 2: 12).

13. **Who dreamed a dream of grapes?**
    Pharaoh's butler (Gen. 40: 9-11).

14. **Who dreamed of a great tree?**
    Nebuchadnezzar (Dan. 4: 10-18).

15. **Who were told in a dream to go to Egypt?**
    Joseph and Mary.

16. **Who dreamed of seven bad ears of corn eating up seven good ears of corn?**
    Pharaoh (Gen. 41: 22-24).

17. **Who dreamed of God and the Son of man?**
    Daniel (Dan. 7: 9-14).

18. **Who dreamed about the sheaves of grain doing obeisance to his sheaf?**
    Joseph (Gen. 37: 7).

FISH QUIZ

1. **When were fish first created?**
   On the fifth day of creation (Gen. 1: 20, 21).

2. **Which were considered "clean fish" according to the Mosaic law, and used for food?**
   Fish that had fins and scales (Lev. 11: 9-12).

3. **What nation worshiped a fish-god?**
   The Philistines. Dagon was the "fish-god" (Judg. 16: 23).

4. **Did the Israelites ever worship the image of a fish?**
   No. They were forbidden to make such an image (Deut. 4: 18).

5. **When was it a plague caused all the fish to die in the Nile River?**
   This was one of the plagues at the time of the Exodus (Ex. 7: 21).

6. **What miracle did Jesus perform with fish?**
   He fed a multitude on two different occasions with a few loaves and fishes (Matt. 14: 17; 15: 34).

7. **Where did the people of Jerusalem go to buy their fish?**
   To the fish-gate (Neh. 3: 3; 13: 16).

8. **What is the largest "catch" recorded?**

When the disciples caught 153 large fish in a net (John 21:11).

9. **Where did Jesus get money to pay the tribute tax at one time?**

In the mouth of a fish which Peter was told to catch (Matt. 17:27).

10. **In what sea are there no fish?**

The Dead Sea. It is too salty for fish to live.

11. **What parable of the judgment dealt with fish?**

The parable of the dragnet (Matt 13:47, 48).

12. **Where did Jesus serve the disciples a fish breakfast?**

On the shore of the Sea of Galilee (John 21:9).

13. **What Old Testament character is associated with a fish?**

Jonah.

14. **Did such a person as Jonah ever live?**

He was a prophet during the days of Jeroboam II, when the kingdom of Israel was at its height (2 Kings 14:25).

15. **Did Jesus look upon Jonah as a real person?**

Yes.

16. **How did He honor him?**

By refusing to give to a wicked generation any other symbol than "the sign of Jonah" (Matt. 12:39).

17. **What was "the sign of Jonah"?**

The resurrection. "As Jonah was three days and three nights in the whale's belly; so shall the Son of man be three days and three nights in the heart of the earth" (Matt. 12:39, 40).

18. **What four fishermen did Jesus call to His service?**
Peter, Andrew, James and John (Matt. 4:18, 21).

19. **What promise did He give to them?**
"Follow me, and I will make you fishers of men" (Matt 4:19).

20. **What teaching concerning the goodness of God did Jesus give in connection with a fish?**
"What man is there of you, whom if his son ask bread, will he give him a stone? Or if he ask a fish, will he give him a serpent? If ye, then, being evil, know how to give good gifts unto your children, how much more shall your Father which is in heaven give good things to them that ask him?" (Matt. 7:9-11).

MARRIAGE QUIZ

1. Marriage is primarily a—
Social institution.
Religious institution (Matt. 19:4-6).
Legal contract.

2. Marriage is intended to be—
Lifelong (Rom. 7:2, 3).
A temporary experiment.
As long as people can agree.

3. A Christian is free to marry—
Anybody he pleases.
Only a Christian (2 Cor. 6:14-18; 1 Cor. 7:39).
Any respectable man or woman.

4. A woman whose husband is dead—
Must remain true to him by not remarrying.
May remarry if she wishes (Rom. 7: 2, 3).
Should not get interested in other men.

58

5. A person may be divorced—
    For any cause.
    If they can not agree.
    For adultery only (Matt. 19: 3, 8, 9).

6. Marriages are—
    Only for this world (Matt. 22: 29, 30).
    Primarily for the next world.
    Carried over into heaven.

7. To be unmarried is—
    A great calamity.
    A matter of choice (1 Cor. 7: 8, 9).
    A disgrace.

8. When husbands and wives can not agree—
    They should separate.
    They should be patient (1 Cor. 7: 16).
    They should go ahead and argue.

9. When husband and wife separate, they—
    Should file for divorce.
    Look for a better companion.
    Be reconciled (1 Cor. 7: 10, 11).

10. If a Christian is married to an unbeliever, he should—
    Separate from her.
    Seek to win her to Christ (1 Cor. 7: 13-17).
    Go ahead and divorce her.

11. Marriage is—
    A less holy estate than virginity.
    A holy estate (1 Cor. 7: 28).
    Not a matter of holiness.

12. Marriage—
    Is a guarantee to happiness.
    May be a source of trouble (1 Cor. 7: 28).
    Is a foretaste of heaven.

MONEY QUIZ

1. **What metals were used for coins?**
   Gold, silver, brass (Matt. 10:9).

2. **What amount did Abraham pay for the cave of Machpelah, in which to bury Sarah?**
   Four hundred shekels of silver (Gen. 23:16).

3. **For what amount was Joseph sold?**
   Twenty pieces of silver (Gen. 37:28).

4. **What portion of one's earnings is sacred to Jehovah?**
   The tithe, or one-tenth (Mal. 3:8-10).

5. **What man brought defeat to Israel by stealing silver and gold?**
   Achan (Josh. 7:1-21).

6. **What man's covetousness brought leprosy on him?**
   Gehazi (2 Kings 5:20-27).

7. **What parables did Jesus give about money?**
   The parables of the talents and the pounds (Matt. 25:20; Luke 19:13). Also the parables of the lost coin, hidden treasure, dishonest steward.

8. **How many sparrows could be bought for a farthing?**
   Two (Matt. 10:29).

9. **On one occasion, where did Jesus get money with which to pay tribute?**
   In the mouth of a fish (Matt. 17:24-27).

10. **What was the largest gift placed in the temple treasury?**
    The widow's mites (Mark 12:42-44).

11. **What was the value of the ointment Mary put on Jesus?**
Three hundred pence (John 12:5).

12. **Which one of the twelve stole money from the bag?**
Judas, who was treasurer (John 12:6).

13. **For how many pieces of silver was Jesus betrayed?**
Thirty (Matt. 26:15).

14. **What was done with the money Judas received for betraying Jesus, and which he returned?**
It was used to buy a potter's field (Matt. 27:7).

15. **What was the value of the magic books burned in Ephesus?**
Fifty thousand pieces of silver (Acts 19:19).

PHYSIOLOGY QUIZ

Fill in the blank spaces with a word representing some part of the body.

1. "If thou shalt confess with thy .... the Lord Jesus, and shalt believe in thine .... that God hath raised him from the dead, thou shalt be saved. For with the .... man believeth unto righteousness; and with the .... confession is made unto salvation" (Rom. 10:9, 10).

2. "And if thy right .... offend thee, pluck it out, and cast it from thee: for it is profitable for thee that one of thy members should perish, and not that thy whole body should be cast into hell" (Matt. 5:29).

3. "No man, having put his .... to the plow, and looking back, is fit for the kingdom of God" (Luke 9:62).

4. "But when they came to Jesus, and saw that he was dead already, they brake not his ...." (John 19:33).

5. "And they that passed by railed on him, wagging their ...., and saying, Ah, thou that destroyest the tem-

61

ple, and buildest it in three days, Save thyself, and come down from the cross" (Mark 15:29, 30).

6. "Neither shalt thou swear by thy ...., because thou canst not make one .... white or black" (Matt. 5:36).

7. "Ye have heard that it hath been said, An .... for an ...., and a .... for a ....: But I say unto you, That ye resist not evil: but whosoever shall smite thee on thy right ...., turn to him the other also" (Matt. 5:38, 39).

8. "Though I speak with the .... of men and of angels, and have not charity, I am become as sounding brass, or a tinkling cymbal" (1 Cor. 13:1).

9. "And I put a jewel on thy ...., and ear rings in thine ...., and a beautiful crown upon thine head" (Ezek. 16:12).

10. "This people draweth nigh unto me with their ...., and honoureth me with their ....; but their .... is far from me" (Matt. 15:8).

11. "Blessed are the pure in ....: for they shall see God" (Matt. 5:8).

12. "If any man among you seem to be religious, and bridleth not his ...., but deceiveth his own ...., this man's religion is vain" (Jas. 1:26).

13. "For the .... of the Lord are over the righteous, and his .... are open unto their prayers: but the .... of the Lord is against them that do evil" (1 Pet. 3:12).

14. "And he [God] said, Thou canst not see my ....: for there shall no man see me, and live. And the Lord said, Behold, there is a place by me, and thou shalt stand upon a rock: And it shall come to pass, while my glory passeth by, that I will put thee in a clift of the rock, and will cover thee with my .... while I pass by: and I will take

away mine ...., and thou shalt see my .... parts: but my .... shall not be seen" (Ex. 33: 20-23).

15. "My servant Moses is not so; who is faithful in all mine house. With him will I speak .... to ...., even apparently, and not in dark speeches" (Num. 12:7, 8).

16. "Is my .... shortened at all, that it cannot redeem? or have I no power to deliver?" (Isa. 50:2b).

17. "When I consider thy heavens, the work of they ...., the moon and the stars, which thou hast ordained; What is man, that thou art mindful of him?" (Ps. 8:3, 4).

18. "But whoso shall offend one of these little ones which believe in me, it were better for him that a millstone were hanged about his ...., and that he were drowned in the depth of the sea" (Matt. 18:6).

1. **Mouth, heart.** 2. **Eye.** 3. **Hand.** 4. **Legs.** 5. **Heads.** 6. **Head, hair.** 7. **Eye, tooth, cheek.** 8. **Tongues.** 9. **Nose, ears, head.** 10. **Mouth, lips, heart.** 11. **Heart.** 12. **Tongue, heart.** 13. **Eyes, ears, face.** 14. **Face, hand, hand, back, face.** 15. **Mouth.** 16. **Hand.** 17. **Fingers.** 18. **Neck.**

WHEN THE WORLD WAS YOUNG

True or False Test

1. There were people in the world before Adam. **False.** Paul definitely speaks of Adam as being the first man (1 Cor. 15:45).

2. The Bible says that the earth is only 6,000 years old. **False.** It does not say when the earth was created, but it was back "in the beginning."

3. There were other people in the world besides Adam's family when they were living in Eden. **False.** Adam called his wife "Eve," because she was the "mother of all living" (Gen. 3:20).

4. Night was created before day. **True.** The Hebrew day began in the evening and ended in the daytime (Gen. 1:5).

5. God had somebody to help Him in the creation. **True.** Jesus had a part in creation (Gen. 1:26; John 1:1-4).

6. God created "the hen before the egg." **True** (Gen. 1:20-22).

7. The Bible teaches that one species of life changes into another. **False.** Each brings forth "after its own kind," and that remains true to this day. If one type of life merged into another, there would be millions of examples, but you can always depend on the egg's hatching a chicken instead of an animal (Gen. 1:12).

8. Man was created last because he was of least value. **False.** Man was created in the image of God (Gen. 1:26).

9. Woman committed the first sin. **True** (Gen. 3:6).

10. Man offered the first excuse for doing wrong. **True** (Gen. 3:12).

11. The devil asked the first question recorded in the Bible. **True** (Gen. 3:1).

12. The devil told the first lie. **True** (Gen. 3:4).

13. Abel's sacrifice to God was accepted. **True** (Gen. 4:4).

14. Cain's sacrifice was rejected. **False.** Cain brought no sacrifice as did Abel. His was an offering of grain (Gen. 4:3).

15. Cain's wife was a native of the land of Nod. **False.** She is first mentioned when in the land of Nod. She was a daughter of Adam (Gen. 5:4).

16. God was unjust to Cain in sending him out to be a wanderer. **False.** Cain could have repented, but wouldn't do it (Gen. 4:7).

17. The first city was named after a boy. **True.** (Enoch) (Gen. 4:17).

18. Lamech was the first polygamist. **True** (Gen. 4:19).

64

19. Mahalaleel was the oldest man who ever lived. **False.** It was Methuselah; he is said to have lived 969 years (Gen. 5:27).

20. When Noah was ordered to make an ark, he and his wife were the only righteous persons living. **True.** By calculating ages, it appears their three sons had not yet been born.

21. The ark was the largest boat of ancient times. **True.** Not until the past century were ships made which were larger.

22. It was not fair of God to save only eight people. **False.** The rest wouldn't repent, though Noah preached to them. God could have called off the flood if they had turned to righteousness (2 Pet. 2:5).

23. The animals were tame before the flood. **True** (Gen. 9:2).

24. Animals were not eaten before the flood. **True** (Gen. 1:29; 9:3).

25. The world shall never be destroyed by a great flood again. **True** (Gen. 9:11-17).

THE DAYS OF THE PATRIARCHS

1. **Who was the father of the Hebrew people?**
    Abraham (Gen. 12:1-3).

2. **From what land did he come?**
    Chaldea (Gen. 11:28).

3. **What was his native city?**
    Ur (Gen. 11:28).

4. **What was his wife's name?**
    Sarah (Gen. 11:29).

5. **How did he happen to leave Chaldea?**
    God called him to go into a new land (Gen. 12:1).

6. Which was the principal son of Abraham?
   Isaac (Gen. 17:19).

7. Were there other children?
   Yes (Gen. 25:1-19).

8. With whom did God make a covenant?
   Isaac (Gen. 17:19).

9. Who was Lot?
   A nephew of Abraham.

10. Did not God tell Abraham to leave all his relatives?
   Yes, but Lot came along anyway (Gen. 12:1-5).

11. Did any good come of this?
   No. Lot was an occasion for trouble (Gen. 13:5-12).

12. How did Abraham settle his trouble with Lot?
   By letting him have the choice of the land (Gen. 13:8-11).

13. Where did Lot decide to dwell?
   In Sodom (Gen. 13:12).

14. What became of Sodom?
   It was destroyed because of its great wickedness (Gen 19:24).

15. Was Lot destroyed, also?
   No. Lot was warned by angels to flee (Gen. 19:12, 13).

16. What happened to Lot's wife?
   She disobeyed the orders not to look back at the burning city, and became a pillar of salt (Gen. 19:26).

17. What did Jesus have to say concerning Lot's wife?
   He said, "Remember Lot's wife" (Luke 17:32).

18. Who was Ishmael?

A son of Abraham by his Egyptian wife, Hagar. (Gen. 16:3, 15).

19. What became of Hagar and Ishmael?

They were sent away, after the birth of Isaac, for being insolent (Gen. 21:8-13).

20. Who were the descendants of Ishmael?

The Arabs. There were twelve tribes (Gen. 25:16).

21. How old was Sarah when she died?

One hundred twenty-seven years old. She is the only woman whose age is mentioned.

22. Where was she buried?

In the cave of Machpelah, which Abraham bought from Ephron, the Hittite (Gen. 23:1-20).

23. Where is it located?

Near Hebron (Gen. 23:19).

24. What other great character lived about the time of Abraham?

Job.

25. How do we know that to be the case?

(a) The land of Uz was so called about that time (Job 1:1); (b) Job offered up sacrifices as the head of the family (Job 1:5); (c) Job lived to be 140 years of age.

26. How would the Book of Job rank chronologically with the other books of the Old Testament?

It was the first one written, preceding the Books of Moses by about five hundred years.

27. To whom was Isaac betrothed?

Rebekah (Gen. 24:67).

28. Who were the sons of Isaac?
Jacob and Esau (Gen. 25:27).

29. What foolish thing did Esau do?
Sold his birthright for a mess of pottage (Gen. 25: 29-34).

30. What ruse did Jacob use to get his father's blessing?
He disguised himself so his father would think he was Esau (Gen. 27:1-40).

31. Did he get the blessing he wanted?
No. He did not get the "blessing of Abraham" as he expected. That came later (Gen. 28:3, 4).

32. What did Esau do about this?
He vowed he would slay Jacob (Gen. 27:41).

33. How did Jacob get out of the predicament?
His mother decided it would be a good time for him to go visiting (Gen. 27:42-45).

34. What did Jacob's father suggest?
That he ought to go to Mesopotamia and find a wife among his relatives (Gen. 28:1-5).

35. Was not the marrying of close relatives forbidden?
No. Not until the giving of the Mosaic law several hundred years later. Many tribes in those days felt it was a mistake to seek a wife among strangers.

36. Are there examples of marriage of relatives?
The family of Adam; Abraham, who married his half-sister (Gen. 20:12), and Nahor, who married his aunt (Gen. 11:29).

37. Why was it permitted then?
Possibly because in those days the blood of the race was pure, and accumulated weaknesses did not curse the offspring of such marriages, as is the case today.

38. With whom did Jacob become infatuated?

With Rachel, daughter of Laban, his uncle (Gen. 29:18).

39. What offer did he make to Laban?

To serve him seven years for his daughter (Gen. 29:18).

40. How did Laban trick him?

When the veil was removed, he found he had married the older daughter, Leah (Gen. 29:25).

41. How did Jacob get the one he loved?

By working seven more years for Laban (Gen. 29:27, 28).

42. How many wives did Jacob finally have?

Four. He married the handmaids of Rachel and Leah.

43. How many children did Jacob have?

Thirteen. Twelve sons and one daughter, Dinah (Gen. 30:21).

44. Which was the favorite son of Jacob?

Joseph (Gen. 37:4).

45. What unusual experience did Jacob have when he returned to Canaan?

He wrestled with an angel (Gen. 32:24-31).

46. What happened when Jacob met his brother, Esau?

They made peace with each other (Gen. 33:4).

47. How did Jacob show his favoritism to Joseph?

By making him a coat of many colors (Gen. 37:3).

48. What was the effect on the brothers?

They hated him and would not speak peaceably to him (Gen. 37:4).

49. How did the brothers get even with Joseph?
By selling him as a slave (Gen. 37: 27, 28).

50. What became of Joseph after becoming a slave?
He became a trusted servant and was promoted by Potiphar, his master (Gen. 39: 1-4).

51. What misfortune came to Joseph?
He was thrown into prison on a false charge (Gen. 39: 7-20).

52. How did Joseph get out of prison?
Through interpreting dreams, including one that Pharaoh had (Gen. 41: 25).

53. How did Pharaoh reward Joseph?
By setting him over the whole kingdom (Gen. 41: 39-45).

54. How did Joseph save the people of Egypt?
By storing up grain during the seven good years (Gen. 41: 48).

55. What happened to Joseph's brethren when the famine came?
They came to Egypt to buy food and were recognized by him (Gen. 42: 8).

56. How did Joseph treat his brethren?
He forgave them instead of punishing them (Gen. 42: 1-15).

57. What did Joseph do for his people?
He sent for his old father, and had the brothers and their families move to the best part of Egypt (Gen. 45: 17-20).

58. How long did the Israelites stay in the land of Egypt?
Four hundred thirty years (Ex. 12: 40).

THE EXODUS

1. What happened to the Israelites during their sojourn in Egypt?

There arose a king who "knew not Joseph," and he made slaves of the Israelites (Ex. 1:8-14). Aahmes, a native prince, drove out the Shepherd Kings and set up again an Egyptian dynasty. Since the Israelites were a shepherd people, he was afraid they might help the Shepherd Kings get control of the country again.

2. What order did he give concerning the Israelites?

The boy babies were to be killed (Ex. 1:16).

3. Whom did God call to lead the Israelites out of Egypt?

Moses (Ex. 1:10).

4. What do we know of Moses' early life?

He was found in the bulrushes where his mother had placed him for safety, and adopted by the daughter of Pharaoh (Ex. 2:1-10).

5. How did Moses come to leave his princely heritage?

He attacked an Egyptian taskmaster who was brutally treating one of the Hebrews, and had to flee for his life (Ex. 2:15).

6. Where did Moses go?

To the land of Midian where he kept the flocks for Jethro, and married one of his daughters (Ex. 2:15-22).

7. In what way did God speak to Moses?

He spoke from the fire of a burning bush, and commanded him to go lead Israel out of Egypt (Ex. 3:1-22).

8. Did Moses respond readily?

No. He was afraid, and made excuses (Ex. 4:1-9).

9. What assistance did God provide?

He gave Moses the power of miracles, and his brother Aaron was to be a helper (Ex. 4:1-17).

10. What was the purpose of sending the plagues upon the land of Egypt?

That God might be seen as greater than all the gods of Egypt (Ex. 7:5; 8:22; 9:14).

11. Was God just in "hardening Pharaoh's heart"?

God had a purpose in doing this (Ex. 7:1-6). The choice Pharaoh had to make was whether or not he would let the Israelites go. In matters of personal salvation, God never hardens the heart of a man; that comes from resisting the truth.

12. What feast was instituted in connection with the Exodus?

The Passover (Ex. 12:3-11). It was also called the "Feast of the Unleavened Bread" (Ex. 12:17).

13. What was the purpose of it?

It was a memorial of the time when the Lord "passed over" the Israelites, when the first-born of the Egyptians were taken by the angel of death (Ex. 12:14).

14. How was it to be observed?

By the eating of unleavened bread, bitter herbs and a lamb (Ex. 12:8).

15. When was it observed?

In the first month of the Jewish year, which was in March, beginning with the fourteenth day and continuing for a week.

16. What did Pharaoh do when the Israelites left?

He sent the army to pursue them and bring them back (Ex. 14:9).

17. How did the Israelites escape?

Moses caused the Red Sea to part, and they walked through (Ex. 14:21). Previously they had been protected by a pillar of cloud by day and a pillar of fire by night (Ex. 13:21).

18. What became of the Egyptians?

They were drowned in the sea (Ex. 14:25-27).

19. What happened after the crossing of the Red Sea?

The Israelites wandered in the wilderness of Shur for three days, unable to find water. At Marah, they found water, which, after being purified by Moses, was usable (Ex. 15:22, 23).

20. What did they find at Elim?

An oasis of twelve springs and seventy palm trees (Ex. 15:27).

21. What happened in the "wilderness of sin"?

The people murmured for "the flesh-pots of Egypt" (Ex. 16:1-3). God provided them with heavenly manna and quails (Ex. 16:13).

22. How long was manna provided?

For forty years, until they came to the promised land (Ex. 16:35).

23. What notable institution was begun in the "wilderness of sin"?

The observance of the Sabbath (Ex. 16:23).

24. Is there any record that the people of God ever observed the Sabbath before?

No.

25. What was the meaning of the Sabbath?

It was a reminder that God had delivered them out of Egypt (Deut. 5:15).

26. **Would the Sabbath, then, have any significance to those who were not Israelites?**
   No. God said, "It is a sign between me and the children of Israel for ever" (Ex. 31:17).

27. **What took place at Rephidim?**
   The people demanded water of Moses, and he provided it by striking a rock (Ex. 17:1).

28. **What happened when the Amalekites attacked the Israelites?**
   God gave the Israelites the victory, and vowed He would wipe out this robber tribe which had attacked Israel without cause (Ex. 17:14).

29. **Who suggested that Moses set up a system of courts to judge the people?**
   Jethro, the father-in-law of Moses (Ex. 18:13-26).

30. **Where did Moses receive the law of God?**
   On Mt. Sinai (Ex. 19:20).

31. **Where do we find the Ten Commandments?**
   Ex. 20:1-17.

32. **On what were they written?**
   On tables of stone (Ex. 24:12).

33. **Were there other laws than the Ten Commandments?**
   Many of them. They are found in the Books of Exodus, Leviticus, Numbers and Deuteronomy.

34. **What sin did the Israelites commit in Moses' absence?**
   They worshiped a golden calf (Ex. 32:1-8).

35. **Who made the golden calf?**
   Aaron (Ex. 32:1-5).

36. **What became of the golden calf?**
   Moses ground it into powder, put it in water and made the people drink it (Ex. 32:20).

74

37. What unusual building was erected at Mt. Sinai?
    The tabernacle (Ex. 25:8).

38. Where did Moses get his plans for the tabernacle?
    The pattern was given by God (Ex. 25:8, 9).

39. Where did they get the materials to use?
    The people gave them willingly (Ex. 25:1-7).

40. When was the tabernacle dedicated?
    On the first day of the second year (Ex. 40:17-38).

41. Who were the priests and high priest?
    Aaron and his sons and all male descendants (Ex. 28:1).

42. Who guided the Israelites through the wilderness?
    Hobab, son of Jethro (Reuel), and brother-in-law of Moses (Num. 10:32). His descendants were called Kenites (Judg. 1:16).

43. What happened to Miriam after the Israelites left Sinai?
    She complained about Moses having a Cushite wife and was temporarily smitten with leprosy (Num. 12:1-15).

44. How many spies were sent into the promised land?
    Twelve. They were gone forty days, and returned bringing samples of the fruits of the land (Num. 13:23).

45. What report did they make?
    They were impressed with it, but were afraid of the giants who occupied part of the land (Num. 13:27-29, 31-33).

46. Were there not two of them who gave a different report?
    Yes. Caleb and Joshua were for taking possession of the land immediately (Num. 13:30).

47. **How did the people receive these reports?**

They listened to the ten and, rebelling against Moses, were ready to return to Egypt (Num. 14: 1-19).

48. **What did God decree concerning them?**

They should not be allowed to go in and possess it (Num. 14: 23-35). Only those under twenty years of age would have that privilege. The others must spend forty years of wandering in the wilderness.

49. **What was the reaction of the people?**

When they found out they couldn't go in, they changed their minds, and decided to do so anyway. They made the attempt, and were attacked by the Amalekites (Num. 14: 39-45).

50. **After years of wandering, what sin did Moses commit?**

They were not able to find water, and the people pestered him until, in his anger, he smote a rock to provide water without giving God the credit for it (Num. 20: 1-11).

51. **How did God punish Moses for this sin?**

By refusing to allow him to lead the people into the promised land (Num. 20: 12).

52. **Did the Israelites find any opposition to entering the land?**

The Edomites refused to let them pass through their territory (Num. 20: 14-21).

53. **What did they do then?**

They had to go many miles around a mountain range and come to the land by the east side of the Jordan.

54. **What took place on Mt. Hor?**

Aaron, the high priest, died and Eleazar succeeded him (Num. 20: 22-29).

55. What incident took place at Punon?

The people rebelled against Moses and God, and He sent fiery serpents among them. In order that the righteous die not, Moses was instructed to make a brazen serpent, and these might look upon it and live if they were bitten (Num. 21:4-9; see John 3: 14, 15).

56. What took place when they reached the Pisgah range of mountains?

Moses found the Israelites confronted with Sihon, king of the Amorites, but they were victorious over his army. Later, they fought with Og, a giant king, and his army and were again victorious (Num. 21: 21-35).

57. What plan did the Moabites use against Israel?

They brought a prophet, Balaam, to curse Israel, but God required him to bless them instead (Num. 22: 1—24:25).

58. Before they began the conquest of Canaan, what was done?

The people were numbered, and only Caleb, Joshua and Moses were left of those who lived forty years before, who were forbidden to enter (Num. 26:64, 65).

59. Was Moses allowed to go in?

No. God had said he should not. He was allowed to see the promised land, but not enter.

60. Was not this unjust, after all Moses had suffered?

No, for he got something better—an acceptable entrance into the heavenly country.

61. Who was appointed to take his place?

Joshua (Num. 27:15-22).

62. Where did Moses die?

On Mt. Nebo (Deut. 34:7).

63. What was Joshua's first move?

He sent spies across the Jordan to Jericho (Josh. 2:9-11).

64. How did the Israelites cross the Jordan?

When the priests bearing the ark stepped into the water, the river parted and let them walk across (Josh. 4:18-20).

65. What took place after they crossed the Jordan?

The manna, which had been provided for forty years, now ceased. They must live through their own efforts henceforth (Josh. 5:12).

66. How did they capture Jericho?

They marched around the city once daily for six days; on the seventh they went around it seven times and God caused the walls to fall (Josh. 6:1-21).

67. What was the next city they attacked?

Ai. At first they failed, because Achan sinned by taking money and garments in Jericho, which had been decreed sacred to the Lord. When Achan was punished, victory came (Josh. 7:1—8:23).

68. What other conquests did they make?

They met several armies and defeated them, eventually gaining control of most of the country (Josh. 9:1—12-24).

69. What did they do with the land?

Divided it among the twelve tribes (Josh. 13:1—19:51).

THE MOSAIC LAW

1. If a man killed another person, he was—
   Sent to the galleys.
   Put to death (Ex. 21:12).
   Required to pay the relatives a certain sum.

2. Every seventh year the land was to—
   Remain unused (Lev. 25:4).
   Loaned to the poor without charge.
   Be sown with a different crop.

3. Kings were forbidden to have—
   Camels.
   Elephants.
   Horses (Deut. 17:16).

4. A stubborn, rebellious son was to be—
   Disinherited.
   Sold as a slave.
   Stoned to death (Deut. 21:18-21).

5. A woman was forbidden to—
   Wear jewelry.
   Wear men's clothing (Deut. 22:5).
   Pluck her eyebrows.

6. Children were to be taught the law by the—
   Scribes.
   Parents (Deut. 6:7).
   Priests.

7. Clean animals were—
   Those that did not wallow in the mire.
   Those that part the hoof and chew the cud (Deut. 14:6).
   Those that were fed clean food.

8. Graven images were to be—
   Used in art galleries.
   Forbidden (Lev. 26:1).
   Reserved only for kings.

9. If a child cursed his father or mother, he was—
   Put to death (Ex. 21:17).
   Called to account by the rabbis.
   Required to go to jail for a week.

10. If a man stole a sheep from somebody—
    He was fined a certain amount.
    He had to pay the owner four sheep in return (Ex. 22:1).
    He was hanged as a robber.

11. If a man lent money to a poor person—
    He could take no interest (Ex. 22:25).
    He could not demand more than six per cent.
    He might take usury.

12. The Sabbath day was commanded—
    Because God rested on the Sabbath day.
    Because the people needed recreation.
    To remember God's delivering them from Egypt (Deut. 5:15).

13. The penalty for eating blood in the meat was—
    Death (Lev. 17:10-14).
    Forty stripes.
    A fine of one hundred shekels.

14. Tatoos were—
    Greatly admired.
    Strictly forbidden (Lev. 19:28).
    Reserved for members of the Sanhedrin.

15. If a man knocked out a man's tooth—
>
> The nearest relative might kill him.
>
> **He might have his own tooth knocked out** (Lev. 24:20).
>
> He might be sentenced by the judge.

16. In the matter of giving to God, a person was required—
>
> To bring five shekels.
>
> **Bring the tithe** (Lev. 27:30, 31).
>
> Give as he was able.

17. If a person accidentally slew another, he was to—
>
> **Flee to a city of refuge** (Num. 35:11).
>
> Confess to the high priest.
>
> Flee from the country.

18. If Israel, as a nation, departed from the law, they would be—
>
> Visited by a plague of cholera.
>
> **Scattered among all the nations** (Deut. 4:27).
>
> Required to read the Bible through in atonement.

19. The men were required to go to the tabernacle or temple—
>
> **Three times a year** (Deut. 16:16).
>
> Only on holidays.
>
> Every Sabbath day.

20. Fortune tellers were to be—
>
> Sought for advice on New Year's Eve.
>
> **Put to death** (Lev. 20:27).
>
> Driven from the land.

21. Honoring one's parents brought—
>
> **Added years** (Ex. 20:12).
>
> Great honor.
>
> Wealth.

22. Kidnaping was punished by—
> **Death** (Ex. 21:16).
> Exile.
> Imprisonment.

23. The poor were to be cared for by—
> Direct relief from the temple treasury.
> **Gleaning after the reapers** (Deut. 19:9).
> Being provided with work.

24. If an enemy's ox was found loose—
> It might be confiscated.
> **It should be returned to him** (Ex. 23:4).
> It should be held for a reasonable reward.

THE JUDGES

1. **Who were the Judges?**
> After the conquest of Canaan, and the death of Joshua, the land was without centralized leadership. "In those days there was no king in Israel, but every man did that which was right in his own eyes" (Judg. 17:6). The Judges were not judges in the sense that we think of judges, but rather were military leaders who brought deliverance from the enemies of Israel.

2. **How many were there?**
> Fifteen.

3. **What were their names?**

Othniel	Abimelech	Elon
Ehud	Tola	Abdon
Shamgar	Jair	Samson
Deborah	Jephthah	Eli
Gideon	Ibzan	Samuel

4. Why were enemies allowed to trouble Israel?

Because the people forgot the Lord, and followed other gods. Then Jehovah raised up a judge to deliver them, and was with the judge (Judg. 2:16-18); yet they turned back to idolatry as soon as the judge had died.

5. What held the tribes together during this time?

A common ancestry, language and religion. The tabernacle was at Shiloh; there was one altar and one high priest; there were daily sacrifices and the three annual feasts.

6. What did Othniel do?

He led the people in throwing off the yoke of the Assyrians, whom they had served eight years (Judg. 3:8, 9).

7. What did Ehud do?

He helped deliver Israel from the Moabites (Judg. 3:15-30).

8. What do we know of Shamgar?

Very little. He delivered Israel from the Philistines (Judg. 3:31).

9. Who was Deborah?

She was the one judge who was a woman. She inspired Barak to lead an army against the Canaanites, who had conquered Israel. They overcame Sisera in the valley of Esdraelon.

10. How did Deborah celebrate the victory?

By writing a song (Judg. 5:1-31).

11. Who was Gideon?

He called himself "the least in his father's house" and said his family was "the poorest in Manasseh" (Judg. 6:15).

12. Where was he when God called him to lead Israel?

In a wine-press, threshing wheat, since it was necessary to hid it from the Midianites who were in control of the country (Judg. 6:11).

13. Did he respond readily?

No. After the angel departed, he asked God for two signs to be sure that He really meant it (Judg. 6:36-40).

14. How many people gathered at the call of Gideon?

Thirty-two thousand (Judg. 7:3).

15. Was that number sufficient to meet the Midianites?

There were too many. All who were afraid were allowed to go home; twenty-two thousand went. There were still too many; they would not feel the deliverance was from God. So when they went to the river to drink, those "that lappeth of the water with his tongue, as a dog lappeth" were noted and set apart. These three hundred were to win the victory.

16. What plan was used?

Each was given a trumpet, torch and pitcher. At the appointed time the pitchers were broken, the torches revealed and the trumpets blown. Ordinarily there was only one trumpet to a company, and the Midianites thought they were surrounded by a mighty host; in the confusion of the darkness they slew each other and Israel was victorious without striking a blow (Judg. 7:1-25).

17. From whom did Abimelech deliver Israel?

Nobody. Abimelech, supported by the men of Shechem, slew the sons of Gideon and ruled over Israel about three years. He was killed in leading an attack upon the city of Thebez (Judg. 9:1-57).

18. What fable was told in connection with Abimelech?

Jotham's fable of the trees seeking a king (Judg. 9:7-15).

19. What do we know of Tola?

Only that he judged Israel twenty-three years. It was apparently a time of peace (Judg. 10:1, 2).

20. What do we know of Jair?

Very little. He judged Israel twenty-two years (Judg. 10:3-5).

21. From whom did Jephthah deliver Israel?

From the Ammonites, with whom they had trouble for about eighteen years (Judg. 10:8).

22. What foolish vow did Jephthah make?

He vowed he would sacrifice to the Lord the first thing that came forth from his house upon his victorious return (Judg. 11:30).

23. Did God ask or approve such a vow?

No (Jer. 7:31). Human sacrifice was never approved.

24. What was the result of it?

His daughter came to meet him, to his horror and sorrow. Perhaps he expected a goat or a dog (Judg. 11:34).

25. How long did Ibzan rule Israel?

Seven years (Judg. 12:8-10).

26. What do we know of Elon?

Only that he judged Israel for ten years (Judg. 12:11, 12).

27. What do we know of Abdon?

He judged Israel eight years (Judg. 12:14).

28. Who delivered Israel from the Philistines, after forty years of oppression?

Samson.

29. For what will Samson be remembered?

For his great strength and great weakness (Judg. 13: 1—16: 31).

30. What unusual way did Samson have of getting even with the Philistines?

He caught three hundred foxes, set fire to their tails and turned them loose in their grain fields (Judg. 15: 4, 5).

31. What Moabite woman cast her lot with Israel during the days of the Judges?

Ruth.

32. What do we know of Eli?

His sons were wicked and unworthy of succeeding him as a judge (Judg. 2: 12-17). God did not approve of Eli for not restraining them (Judg. 3: 13). The Philistines came against the Israelites, and thinking victory would come if they took the ark of the covenant into the battle, they did so and it was captured by the Philistines. When Eli heard of it, he fainted and his neck was broken in falling (Judg. 4: 18).

33. Who was Samuel?

He was the last of the judges, and a prophet, as well. He was dedicated to the Lord as an infant, and was brought up in the tabernacle. God sent a message by him to Eli when he was just a child. When he came to be an old man, his sons were unworthy to be judges and the people demanded a king. At the direction of God, he anointed Saul first king of Israel (1 Samuel).

THE KINGS

1. **Name the first three kings of Israel.**
   Saul. David. Solomon.

2. **After the division of the kingdom at the death of Solomon, about 937 B. C., the "ten tribes" to the north became known as the Kingdom of Israel, while the "two" to the south became known as the Kingdom of Judah.**

Kings of Israel (937-722 B. C.)

1. Jeroboam
2. Nadab
3. Baasha
4. Elah
5. Zimri
6. Omri
7. Ahab
8. Ahaziah
9. Jehoram
10. Jehu
11. Jehoahaz
12. Jehoash (Joash)
13. Jeroboam II
14. Zechariah
15. Shallum
16. Menahem
17. Pekahiah
18. Pekah
19. Hoshea

Kings of Judah (937-586 B. C.)

1. Rehoboam
2. Abijam
3. Asa
4. Jehoshaphat
5. Jehoram (Joram)
6. Ahaziah (Azariah)*
7. Joash (Jehoash)
8. Amaziah
9. Azariah (Uzziah)
10. Jotham
11. Ahaz
12. Hezekiah
13. Manasseh
14. Amon
15. Josiah
16. Jehoahaz (Shallum)
17. Jehoiakim
18. Jehoiachin
19. Zedekiah

* Upon the death of Ahaziah, his mother, Athaliah, daughter of Jezebel, seized the throne and reigned as queen for about six years.

3. **Which king took Jerusalem from the Jebusites, and made it the capital of Israel?**
   David (2 Sam. 5:6, 7).

4. **Which king went to a fortune teller to find out what his fate was going to be?**

    Saul (1 Sam. 28:7-20).

5. **Do fortune teller have the power to foretell the future?**

    No. They are only pretenders. When God really allowed the spirit of Samuel to return to give a message to Saul, the woman was terribly frightened (1 Sam. 28:12). God forbade fortune tellers even to live in the land of Israel (Lev. 19:31). Saul assured her no harm would come (1 Sam. 28:9, 10).

6. **Which man became king by murdering the king, and ruled seven days before burning himself alive in the palace rather than be captured by his rebellious soldiers?**

    Zimri (1 Kings 16:15-20).

7. **Who was king when Elijah brought a three-year drought on Israel?**

    Ahab (1 Kings 17:1—18:1).

8. **Which king disguised himself when he went into battle, but was killed by an arrow?**

    Ahab (1 Kings 22:30-36).

9. **Which queen painted her eyes and had a hair-do that she might save her life by making an impression on the conqueror, Jehu?**

    Jezebel (2 Kings 9:30-34).

10. **Which king had an ivory palace?**

    Ahab (1 Kings 22:39).

11. **Which king had an ivory throne, overlaid with gold, with twelve lions on the steps leading up to the throne?**

    Solomon (1 Kings 10:18-20).

12. **Which king had as his queen an Egyptian princess?**

    Solomon (1 Kings 3:1).

13. Which king was so self-conscious that he hid among the baggage at the time he was chosen king?

    Saul (1 Sam. 10:22).

14. Which man became king because the king's son was his friend and saved his life?

    David (1 Sam. 19:1—20:42.

15. Which king destroyed the brazen serpent which Moses had made hundreds of years before, because the people were worshiping it?

    Hezekiah (2 Kings 18:4).

16. Which king was kind to a lame prince, though an heir to his throne by being a grandson of Saul?

    David. He was kind to Mephibosheth, son of Jonathan, out of love for his father (2 Sam. 9:1-10).

17. Who was king when the angel of death smote the Assyrian invaders outside the city of Jerusalem?

    Hezekiah (2 Kings 19:35).

18. What two kings were killed at the same time?

    Kings Joram of Israel and Ahaziah of Judah (2 Kings 9:24-26).

19. The story of which kings is told on the famous Moabite Stone, written by Mesha, king of Moab?

    Omri and Ahab (2 Kings 3:4f).

20. Which king was known for his swift driving?

    Jehu (2 Kings 9:20).

21. Which king pouted because a man would not sell him a vineyard?

    Ahab (1 Kings 21:4).

22. Which king made two golden calves for the people to worship?

    Jeroboam (1 Kings 12:28, 29).

23. **Which king lost most of his kingdom by following the advice of his smart-alec friends?**
     Rehoboam (1 Kings 12:1-20).

24. **Which king "made silver to be as stones in Jerusalem"?**
     Solomon (1 Kings 10:27).

25. **Which king had his head cut off, and his body hung on the walls of Beth-shan?**
     Saul (1 Sam. 31:9, 10).

26. **Which king had a son so handsome he stole the hearts of the people, and headed a rebellion against his father?**
     David (2 Sam. 15:1-14).

27. **Which king was smitten with leprosy because he attempted to do the office of a priest and burn incense in the temple?**
     Uzziah (2 Chron. 26:16-23).

28. **Which king wanted to build the temple, but was not allowed to do so?**
     David (1 Chron. 17:1-15).

29. **Did David, then, have no part in building the temple?**
     He got materials together so that Solomon might the more easily complete it (1 Chron. 22:1-19).

30. **Which king was once a worshiper of God, but backslid?**
     Joash (2 Chron. 24:17-27).

31. **Which king was sick, and prayed for additional years and fifteen more were granted?**
     Hezekiah (Isa. 38:1-5).

32. **Which king conquered Jerusalem, and took away the golden shields from the temple?**
     Shishak, king of Egypt (2 Chron. 12:9).

33. **Which king died of foot trouble because he preferred to depend on the physicians rather than call on God?**
     Asa (2 Chron. 16:12).

THE PROPHETS

1. **How many books of prophecy are there?**
   Seventeen. Five are known as major prophets and twelve as minor prophets.

2. **In the days of what king did Isaiah have a vision of heaven?**
   Uzziah (Isa. 6:1-10).

3. **Which prophet has been called "the weeping prophet"?**
   Jeremiah.

4. **Which prophet told something of the times of the end?**
   Daniel (Dan. 12:1-3).

5. **Which prophet gave a very complete picture of the Messiah?**
   Isaiah (Isaiah 53).

6. **Which prophet was set as a "watchman for Israel"?**
   Ezekiel (Ezek. 33:7).

7. **Which prophet carried a message of doom to Nineveh?**
   Jonah (Jonah 3:4).

8. **Which prophet had a vision of "a valley of dry bones"?**
   Ezekiel (Ezek. 37:1-14).

9. **To which prophet did the angel, Gabriel, appear?**
   Daniel (Dan. 9:21).

10. **Who was the last prophet of Old Testament times?**
    Malachi.

11. **Which prophet mentioned some one being betrayed for thirty pieces of silver, and the money going unto the potter?**
    Zechariah (Zech. 11:12, 13).

12. Which prophet gives the story of a Son whose name should be called Immanuel?

   Isaiah (Isa. 7:14).

13. Which prophet spoke of the Ephraimites as being "half baked"?

   Hosea (Hos. 7:8).

14. Which prophet foretold the outpouring of God's Spirit, which was manifest on Pentecost?

   Joel (Joel 2:28).

15. Which prophet condemned the people for living in nice houses, and letting the Lord's house be desolate?

   Haggai (Hag. 1:4, 10).

16. Which prophet had the vision of a "flying roll"?

   Zechariah (Zech. 5:1).

17. Which prophet attributed the woes of the people to their withholding the tithe?

   Malachi (Mal. 3:8-10).

18. Which prophet told of a messenger of the Lord who would come and prepare the way?

   Malachi (Mal. 3:1).

19. Which prophet read the "handwriting on the wall"?

   Daniel (Dan. 5:5-31).

20. Which prophet was made prime minister of Persia?

   Daniel (Dan. 6:1-3).

21. Which prophet was "neither a prophet nor son of a prophet" when God called him?

   Amos (Amos 7:14).

22. Which prophet saw the Lord with a "plumb line"?

   Amos (Amos 7:7).

23. Which prophet foretold the birthplace of Christ?
   Micah (Mic. 5:2).

24. Which prophet had a dream of Him who was "the Ancient of days"?
   Daniel (Dan. 7:9-14).

25. Which prophet told of the time when "the earth shall be filled with the knowledge of the glory of the Lord, as the waters cover the sea"?
   Habakkuk (Hab. 2:14).

26. Which prophet had the vision of "a ram and a he-goat"?
   Daniel (Dan. 8:1-14).

27. Which prophet had the vision of "a man with a measuring-rod"?
   Ezekiel (Ezek. 40:1f).

28. Which prophet wrote the Book of Lamentations?
   Jeremiah.

29. Which prophet said "though your sins be as scarlet, they shall be as white as snow"?
   Isaiah (Isa. 1:18).

30. Which prophet said, "Is there no balm in Gilead? is there no physician there?"
   Jeremiah (Jer. 8:22).

31. Which prophet said, "Can the Ethiopian change his skin, or the leopard his spots?"
   Jeremiah (Jer. 13:23).

32. Which prophet said, "Will a man rob God? Yet ye have robbed me"?
   Malachi (Mal. 3:8).

33. Which prophet gave the prophecy, "they shall look upon me whom they have pierced"?
   Zechariah (Zech. 12:10).

34. Which prophet said, "Let judgment run down as waters, and righteousness as a mighty stream"?

> Amos (Amos 5:24).

35. Which prophet said, "For they have sown the wind, and they shall reap the whirlwind"?

> Hosea (Hos. 8:7).

36. Which prophet said, "They that turn many to righteousness shall shine as the stars for ever and ever"?

> Daniel (Dan. 12:3).

37. Which prophet quoted God as saying, "When I say unto the wicked, O wicked man, thou shalt surely die; if thou dost not speak to warn the wicked from his way, that wicked man shall die in his iniquity; but his blood will I require at thy hand"?

> Ezekiel (Ezek. 33:8).

38. Which prophet gave us the story of those who say, "Peace, peace, when there is no peace"?

> Jeremiah (Jer. 8:11).

39. Which prophet said, "Your iniquities have separated between you and your God, and your sins have hid his face from you, that he will not hear"?

> Isaiah (Isa. 59:2).

40. Which prophet said, "Wherefore do ye spend money for that which is not bread? and your labour for that which satisfieth not?"

> Isaiah (Isa. 55:2).

41. Of which prophet was it said, "And no manner of hurt was found upon him, because he believed in his God"?

> Daniel (Dan. 6:23).

42. Which prophet gave the proverb, "The fathers have eaten sour grapes, and the children's teeth are set on edge"?

> Ezekiel (Ezek. 18:2).

43. Through which prophet did God say, "I desired mercy, and not sacrifice; and the knowledge of God more than burnt offerings"?

Hosea (Hos. 6: 6).

44. Who gave us the words, "Prepare to meet thy God"?

Amos (Amos 4: 12).

45. Who quoted God as saying, "I have no pleasure in the death of the wicked; but that the wicked turn from his way and live"?

Ezekiel (Ezek. 33: 11).

46. Who said, "Neither their silver nor their gold shall be able to deliver them in the day of the Lord's wrath"?

Zephaniah (Zeph. 1: 18).

THE FAMILY OF JESUS

1. His mother's name was Mary. **True** (Luke 1: 27).

2. His father's name was Joseph. **False.** Joseph was only His foster-father (Luke 1: 35).

3. Mary had other children after the birth of Jesus. **True.** He was her "first-born" son (Luke 2: 7).

4. Jesus had four brothers. **True** (Matt. 13: 55).

5. Jesus had no sisters. **False** (Matt. 13: 56).

6. The family lived in Bethlehem. **False.** They only went there to register in the census (Luke 2: 4).

7. Joseph was a carpenter. **True** (Matt. 13: 15).

8. Jesus spent His infancy in Egypt. **True** (Matt. 2: 13-15).

9. The parents of Jesus went to Jerusalem every year to attend the Passover. **True** (Luke 2: 49).

10. When separated from His parents in Jerusalem, they found Jesus at the fairgrounds. **False.** In the temple (Luke 2: 46).

11. Jesus, very early in life, felt an urge to be about His heavenly Father's business. **True** (Luke 2:49).

12. Jesus had an understanding beyond His years. **True** (Luke 2:47).

13. Jesus was popular among those who knew Him. **True.** He grew in favor with God and man (Luke 2:52).

14. When Jesus began His work as Messiah, His brothers immediately became His assistants. **False.** They did not become followers until after the resurrection (John 7:5).

15. When Jesus began performing miracles, His superstitious friends thought He was going crazy. **True** (Mark 3:21).

16. Only Mary, of His relatives, went to the cross with Him. **True** (John 19:25).

17. Jesus appeared to James after He was raised. **True** (1 Cor. 15:7).

18. After the resurrection, the family of Jesus gathered with the apostles in the upper room. **True** (Acts 1:14).

19. James became a leader of the church at Jerusalem. **True** (Acts 15:13-20).

20. Two brothers of Jesus wrote books of the Bible. **True** (James and Jude).

AN IMAGINARY INTERVIEW WITH THE LORD

1. **"Where were you born, Lord?"**
    "In Bethlehem of Judea" (Luke 2:1-7).

2. **"When did that take place?"**
    "In the days of Herod. Cæsar Augustus was then ruling in Rome" (Matt. 2:1; Luke 2:1).

3. **"Had you a previous existence before coming to earth?"**
    "Yes. Even before this world was created, I was with God. I assisted in the matter of creation" (John 1:1-3; 16:28).

4. **"How did you happen to come to this world?"**

"God loved the world and wanted it saved; I volunteered to come and die for the sins of men" (John 3:16; 10:11, 17, 18).

5. **"Did you come into a princely palace when you were born?"**

"No. I came into the home of a carpenter" (Matt. 13:55).

6. **"What circumstances attended your birth?"**

"My mother, Mary, and Joseph were in Bethlehem at the time to enroll for the census (Luke 2:1-7). There were no accommodations at the inn, because of the crowd in the city, so my first cradle was a manger. Angels announced my arrival, and shepherds came to pay a call."

7. **"Was there not an attempt made on your life?"**

"Yes. A group of Wise-men who came seeking me stopped at Jerusalem to inquire where I might be found. Herod, who was quite old and anxious to keep the throne in the hands of his family, was fearful lest another should get it, and ordered all the little children of Bethlehem slain" (Matt. 2:16-18).

8. **"How did you escape?"**

"Joseph, my foster-father, was warned by an angel, and we hurried to Egypt, where we stayed until Herod was dead. Fortunately, the Wise-men left gold and other rich gifts with us, so we had adequate provision" (Matt. 2:13-15).

9. **"Where did you go upon returning from Egypt?"**

"To Nazareth, in Galilee. You see, Joseph had formerly lived there" (Luke 2:3).

10. **"How long did you remain in Nazareth?"**

"Until the beginning of my ministry" (Luke 2:51; Mark 1:9).

11. **"What do you consider one of the most interesting events of your boyhood?"**

"A trip I made to Jerusalem at the age of twelve. I got so interested in the temple and its services that I let the folks start home without me. They came back and hunted all over town before thinking of coming to the temple. Even though I was young, a compelling urge was already upon me to do the work of the heavenly Father" (Luke 2:40-52).

12. **"When did you begin your ministry?"**

"During the days of Tiberius Cæsar. Pontius Pilate was then governor of Judea, and Herod Antipas was ruler of Galilee" (Luke 3:1).

13. **"How did you announce yourself to the world?"**

"I had a cousin, John, who did the announcing. He was about six months older than I. Coming, as he did, in the spirit and power of Elijah, and looking much like him, he created such a stir with his message that crowds flocked from all the cities to hear him. You see, it had been almost five hundred years since any prophet's voice had sounded and the land was soon in a state of anticipation" (Matt. 3:1-12).

14. **"When did you appear on the scene?"**

"Several months later. John had been baptizing people, an act to which they submitted as a sign that they were repentant of their sins. But there was another reason. John did not know for sure just who the Messiah was to be, but he was told that upon whomsoever the Spirit of God descended in the form of a dove, that was He. So when I was baptized, not for

98

sin, but as an example, and so this sign might be made manifest, it came to pass" (John 1:19-34; Mark 1:9-11).

15. "What happened then?"

"John announced me as the Lamb of God who had come to take away the sins of the world, and his followers immediately became interested in me (John 1:29-51). John, however, expected that" (John 3:30).

16. "Did you, then, immediately begin your work?"

"No, there was a battle that had to be fought before I could be a leader of others, and for forty days in the wilderness I was tempted of Satan. The struggle was terrific, but I came out victorious" (Matt. 4:1-11).

17. "Did Satan ever attempt to overcome you again?"

"Many times. That fellow is no quitter" (Luke 4:13).

18. "Did you choose the twelve at the beginning of your ministry?"

"No. Followers immediately began to gather around me, being attracted by the signs I did, and no doubt thinking I would attempt a revolution, but in this they were to be disappointed. There were some to whom I gave a personal invitation to be with me, but considerable time passed before I chose the twelve who were to be trained for the work of evangelizing" (John 1:35-51; Mark 1:16-20; 3:13-19).

19. "How did the home-town folks in Nazareth receive you?"

"They didn't. Though none of them could find fault with my life, they thought I had only human parentage, and therefore could not be divine. They looked upon my claim as blasphemy, and sought to kill me" (Luke 4:16-30).

20. **"Where did you make your headquarters, then?"**

"At Capernaum, a thriving industrial center on the north shore of Galilee" (Matt. 4: 13-16).

21. **"Did you get much of a response from the people?"**

"Yes. When they began to hear about my works of healing, they came in great multitudes. One time, after I had fed about five thousand of them, they insisted on making me king. It would be pretty convenient to have a king like that" (Matt. 14: 13-21; John 6: 1-15).

22. **"Did you get any support from the religious leaders of the people?"**

"Very little. The Pharisees became suspicious as soon as John appeared on the scene, and they sent a committee to check up on him (John 1: 19-28). They didn't like our message, for we demanded righteousness of heart, and then, too, we had not been taught in the school of the rabbis. It was not long until they began openly to oppose me" (John 5: 17; Mark 3: 6).

23. **"What plan did you follow, then?"**

"Knowing that sooner or later they would crucify me, I chose twelve men for particular training, who could carry on the work after I was gone" (Mark 3: 13-19; Matt. 5: 1f).

24. **"Did you know at the time that one of them would betray you?"**

"Yes. But he would do it of his own free will, and it was not an unforgivable sin. Many betray me for less than Judas received" (John 6: 64; Matt. 12: 31, 32).

25. "After having taught the disciples, what did you do?"

"I sent them out to get some practical experience. They went out two by two, teaching and performing miracles" (Matt. 9:35—11:1).

26. "Were you ever discouraged with them?"

"Many times. In spite of the many signs I performed, and even the power I entrusted to them, it seemed as if they never would understand or believe" (Matt. 14:31; 16:5-12).

27. "But there must have been times when you were encouraged."

"Yes. I remember that time at Cæsarea Philippi, when I threw out that test question, 'Whom do men say that I am?' and then put the question directly to the disciples. Peter, of course, spoke up first and replied, 'Thou art the Christ, the Son of the living God.' Then there was the time I had that call to go to Lazarus, though opposition was getting so strong it was dangerous to venture into Judea. When the group saw that I was determined to go, Thomas spoke up and said, 'Let us also go, that we may die with him'" (Matt. 16:13-20; John 11:16).

28. "But they were not so bold when the time came for them to face death?"

"No. I'll never forget that scene in Gethsemane. Like frightened deer they fled after the mob came to take me, and I asked that they be spared. Only John stayed with me. But I felt sure they would come back later on" (Matt. 14:50; John 18:8).

29. "You had something to say, I believe, about the time of the end?"

"Yes, but people get it rather mixed up. We were talking about two things that night on the Mount of

101

Olives: when Jerusalem would be destroyed, and when the end of the world would come. I told them when they saw the 'abomination of desolation' [Roman armies] they were to flee to the mountains, and lose no time in doing it. The Christians remembered that and fled to Pella, and their lives were saved. The Jews fled to Jerusalem, thinking it could never be taken, and, after one of the most terrible sieges in history, with more than a million killed or starved, the city was taken and destroyed (Matt. 24:15-22). Then I told them about the end of the world. When they heard of wars and rumors of wars, it was a sign the end was *not* at hand. Before the end comes, the gospel must be taken to the whole world (Matt. 24:4-14; 23-44). That being the case, the end depends upon Christians taking the gospel to every nation; for that reason, neither I nor the angels of heaven know the exact date, and whoever claims he knows is a deceiver" (Matt. 24:4, 36).

30. **"Will everybody know when you return, or just a favored few?"**

"Everybody will know when I come. 'For, as the lightning cometh out of the east and shineth unto the west; so shall also the coming of the Son of man be'" (Matt. 24:27).

31. **"But were not those things to be fulfilled in that generation?"**

"The city was destroyed within that generation (Matt. 24:34). But I plainly stated that the whole world must have the gospel before the end of time should come. That is still in the future."

32. **"People are constantly asking if Judas was lost; they feel he ought not be lost, since it was necessary for the Scriptures to be fulfilled."**

102

"I sorrow yet when I think of Judas. The prophets merely looked forward and recorded what *would* happen; their writing it down didn't make it so. Judas betrayed me of his own free will, and he could have come back, like Peter, and asked forgiveness, but he didn't. Even if Judas hadn't betrayed me, he had other sins which would have caused him to be lost, unless he repented" (John 12: 6).

33. "And what about the man who carried your cross—was he a Negro?"

"Three things brightened the hours of that terrible last day: John's staying with me until the last, and caring for my mother; a penitent robber who turned to me in his dying hour; and Simon, of Cyrene. I shall always be grateful to Simon. Simon lived in a Greek colony on the northern coast of Africa, but that did not make him an African. The Greeks encouraged the Jews to settle in Cyrene, and many of them did so. And it just happened that Simon was coming into the city when the mob seized him. But that chance experience brought him an immortal name. As long as time lasts, he will be remembered as the one who bore my cross. And it proved to be a turning point in his own life, too. He had two sons who became so outstanding in the work of the church that Mark spoke of him as 'the father of Alexander and Rufus'" (Mark 15: 20-23).

34. "And did you come forth from the grave with the same body you had before?"

"Yes, only it was changed somewhat. It was now a 'resurrection body,' and was no longer subject to death. You will recall I raised a number of people from the dead; they had to die over again. But I did not. With that body I ascended to the Father who is in heaven, and thus I became 'the firstfruits of them that slept' (1 Cor. 15:20). This resurrection body had new powers which it did not have before (Luke 24:31; 36-43; John 20:26), and was capable of being changed. It was no longer a slave to matter, but the master of it."

35. "Is it true that you gave the Great Commission only to the twelve, and that others were under no obligation to preach and teach?"

"Did I ever give ridiculous commands to anybody? Twelve men could never evangelize the world. That command was for every Christian, and the Jerusalem church understood it plainly. When persecution caused the disciples to flee from the city, the twelve stayed there, but those who were scattered abroad went everywhere preaching the Word (Acts 8:1-4; Matt. 28:19, 20). May my followers in every century be as faithful as they were."

36. "Thank you, Master, for the words which you spoke, and for the record which has been made of them in the Scriptures."

THE TWELVE

1. James and John at times were self-seeking. **True.** They tried to get Jesus to give them chief places in the kingdom of heaven (Matt. 20:21).

2. Peter was the first follower of Jesus. **False.** Andrew brought Peter to Christ (John 1:40, 41).

3. John was the only one of the twelve who had the courage to stay with Jesus even unto the cross. **True** (John 19:26).

4. James was put to death by Herod. **True** (Acts 12:2).

5. Simon the Zealot was a patriot. **True.** The Zealots were a group of patriots who hated Rome, and sought a chance to be free.

6. Judas was the only one of the twelve not a Galilean. **True.** He was from Judea.

7. Matthew was a lawyer. **False.** He was a taxgatherer.

8. Mark was one of the most prominent of the twelve. **False.** He was not one of the twelve.

9. James wrote a book of the Bible. **False.** It was James, the Lord's brother, who wrote the book.

10. Judas was treasurer of the group. **True** (John 12:6).

11. Matthew wrote one of the Epistles. **False.** He wrote one of the Gospels.

12. Judas stole from the treasury. **True** (John 12:6).

13. James and John once wanted to call down fire on the Samaritans. **True** (Luke 9:54).

14. Peter, James and John went to sleep in Gethsemane. **True** (Mark 14:33-37).

15. Matthias was chosen to take Judas' place. **True** (Acts 1:26).

16. Jesus called the twelve soon after John announced Him as the Messiah. **False.** Considerable time passed before He definitely called the twelve as apostles.

17. Matthew was also called Levi. **True.**

18. James and John had a nickname, "Boanerges." **True** (Mark 3:17).

19. There were two of the twelve named James. **True** (Matt. 10:2).

20. There were two of the twelve named Simon. **True** (Matt. 10:2).

21. Thomas was called "the twin." **True.** He was called "Didymus," which means "the twin" (John 20:24).

22. Judas partook of the Lord's Supper even when planning to betray Christ. **True** (Luke 22:21).

23. Thomas is remembered as being a "doubter." **True** (John 20:25).

24. The twelve were given the power to perform miracles. **True** (Matt. 10:1; Mark 16:17, 18).

25. The twelve were present when Jesus appeared to the group after the resurrection. **False.** Thomas was not present (John 20:24).

26. Jesus provided breakfast for the disciples one morning. **True** (John 21:9, 12).

27. John the Baptist was a member of the twelve. **False.** He never became a follower of Jesus (Matt. 11:11).

28. Jesus told Peter the manner of His death. **True** (John 21:19).

29. Jesus told John that He would not die. **False** (John 21:23).

30. Nathanael didn't have a very good opinion of Nazareth. **True** (John 1:46).

THE ADVENTURES OF THE CHURCH

1. Where did the church have its beginning?
In Jerusalem.

2. How many charter members were there?
About one hundred twenty (Acts 1:15).

3. What was the first official act of the group?
The choosing of an apostle to take the place of Judas (Acts 1:15-26).

4. What qualifications were required of this individual?
He had to be chosen from the group which accompanied Jesus from the time of His baptism until the time He ascended, thus becoming a witness of His resurrection (Acts 1:21, 22).

5. Who was chosen for this high office?
Matthias (Acts 1:26).

6. Did the apostles have a self-perpetuating board?

No. Matthias was chosen by the whole group and not by the eleven. They prayed for the guidance of God in the making of a choice (Acts 1:24-26).

7. When did the church begin its program of evangelism?

On the day of Pentecost when the Spirit was given, which Jesus said would come (Acts 1:4; 2:1-4).

8. How was the coming of the Holy Spirit made manifest?

Tongues as of fire came upon them, there was the sound as of a rushing mighty wind and they began to speak with tongues (Acts 2:1-4).

9. Were the apostles speaking in an "unknown tongue"?

No. They were given the power to speak in other languages, but men of those nations were able to understand it and know the gospel message (Acts 2:5-11).

10. What was the result of the preaching of the twelve?

Three thousand people were converted (Acts 2:41).

11. What did the Pharisees think of what was coming to pass?

They were alarmed at the power which was manifest and in the response of the people, and attempted to stop the disciples (Acts 4:13-21; 5:17-42). The Sadducees joined in with them.

12. How did deacons come to be chosen?

The widows of the Grecian Jews were not receiving their share of support from the common treasury. The apostles felt they could not leave their work to look after it personally, and asked that seven men be chosen to do so (Acts 6:1-6).

13. Were these deacons officers of the church?

No, they were servants of the church. That is what the word means.

14. Were they elected for life?

No. They served the church only as long as the church desired. One of them, Nicolaus, eventually proved to be a backslider.

15. What qualifications were required of them?

(1) Men of good report. (2) Full of the Holy Spirit. (3) Wise (Acts 6:3).

16. Who became the first Christian martyr?

Stephen (Acts 6:7—7:60).

17. What became of the church when persecution started?

All but the twelve fled from Jerusalem (Acts 8:1).

18. Was that the end of the church?

No. Everywhere the disciples went they preached the Word, so churches soon sprang up in many places (Acts 8:4).

19. Who was the leader of the persecution?

Saul (Acts 8:1; 9:1).

20. Where did Philip (the deacon) go?

To Samaria, where he had a fine response (Acts 8:5, 6).

21. Did Philip give any the power of performing miracles?

No. Although he had the power of miracles, he could not pass it on. Peter and John came and conferred the miraculous power of the Spirit (Acts 8:14-17).

22. Were not all Christians to have this power?

The Holy Spirit is a gift unto all Christians. He is an invisible Helper, Comforter and Guide. But all Christians do not have the power of miracles (Acts 2:38; John 15:26; 16:13). We ought to thank God for this invisible Companion, and make use of His services.

23. To what noted man did Philip preach?

The treasurer of Ethiopia (Acts 8:27).

24. Was this man a native Ethiopian?

We are not told. If so, he was a Jewish proselyte. More than likely he was a Jew, who, like Daniel, had risen to great power in Persia, or who, like Joseph, was prime minister of Egypt.

25. What was the result of Philip's teaching?

The man was converted, baptized and went to Ethiopia as the first Christian (Acts 8:26-39).

26. What unusual experience came to Saul?

On the way to Damascus to seek out and arrest Christians, Jesus appeared to him. Temporarily blinded by the brightness of the vision, his sight was restored after three days and he became a Christian and was baptized (Acts 9:1-19).

27. What did Saul do when this great change came to him?

He began immediately to preach the gospel, to the surprise of both friends and enemies (Acts 9:20-22).

28. How did his friends react to this?

They became enemies and sought to kill him (Acts 9:23-25), and his enemies, the Christians, now became his friends and assisted him in escaping from Damascus.

29. Where did Saul go then?

Into Arabia, where he spent about three years (Gal. 1:17, 18). There he was personally taught by Christ (Gal. 1:12, 16-18). This gave him the equivalent of the amount of training received by the twelve.

30. When he returned to Jerusalem what kind of reception did he get?

The disciples, who had not heard of him for three years, and who didn't know what had become of him,

were afraid of him for fear he had not been genuinely
converted and was still an enemy (Acts 9:26-29).

31. Who stood up for Saul?

Barnabas (Acts 9:27).

32. What did Saul do in Jerusalem?

He preached boldly, but the Grecian Jews soon sought
to kill him (Acts 9:29).

33. Where did Saul then go?

The brethren sent him back to Tarsus, his home city
(Acts 9:30).

34. What unusual experience did Peter have?

He was instructed to go to a Gentile, Cornelius, who
lived in Cæsarea and preach to him. This led to his
conversion (Acts 10:1-48).

35. What effect did this have upon the church in Jerusalem?

They called Peter to account for going unto a Gentile,
but he convinced them he went at the command of
God (Acts 11:1-18). They seemed to feel that it was
a special case, however.

**36. Where was the first place that Christians definitely sought
to win the Gentiles?**

Antioch (Acts 11:19-26).

37. Where were the disciples first called Christians?

In Antioch (Acts 11:26).

38. Which was the first one of the twelve to be martyred?

James, the brother of John, who was killed by Herod
Agrippa I (Acts 12:1, 2).

**39. What great leader was brought to Antioch to head up
the work?**

Saul, of Tarsus (Acts 11:25).

110

40. Who went on the first missionary journey?

Saul and Barnabas (Acts 13:2).

41. Where did they go?

First to Cyprus, and then to Asia Minor, in the provinces of Pamphylia and Galatia (Acts 13:4— 14:28).

42. What kind of response did they get?

The Jews opposed them, but the Gentiles welcomed the gospel.

43. What unusual experience took place at Lystra?

At first the people thought they were gods come to earth, when a crippled man was healed. Then came Jews who stirred up the multitude, and Paul was stoned and left for dead, but was revived (Acts 14:8-20).

44. Who accompanied the missionaries?

John Mark, but he soon returned to Jerusalem (Acts 13:13).

45. Where does Luke begin to use the name "Paul" instead of "Saul"?

When Paul is in Cyprus. "Paul" was the Roman name, while "Saul" was the Jewish name.

46. What took place between the first and second missionary journeys?

The Jerusalem Conference, which was called to determine whether it was necessary for the Gentiles to observe the Jewish law. Paul insisted on the freedom of Gentiles from any requirement of the law, and won his point (Acts 15:1-34; Gal. 2:1-21).

47. Who went on the second missionary journey?

Paul and Silas (Acts 15:36-41).

48. Why did not Barnabas go?

Because he insisted on taking John Mark again, and Paul would not permit it (Acts 15:37, 38).

49. What did Barnabas do then?

He took Mark and they went to Cyprus. We do not have the record of their work on this trip (Acts 15:39).

50. Where did Paul and Silas go?

Through Galatia westward to the coast. At Troas, Paul had the vision of a man of Macedonia asking them to come over and help them. They went (Acts 16:1-10).

51. What interesting adventures awaited them?

At Philippi they made their first converts; were wrongfully imprisoned, and "released by an earthquake." At Thessalonica they met with opposition, but found earnest searchers for the truth at Berea. At Athens Paul spoke to the worldly-wise philosophers who scorned the idea of the resurrection, and at Corinth, Paul established a church and worked there for a year and a half (Acts 16:11—18:28).

52. Who went on the third missionary journey?

Paul reported to the church at Antioch, but did not stay long. Going through Galatia, he went to Ephesus, where he had left Aquila and Priscilla to prepare the way (Acts 18:18).

53. What took place in Ephesus before his coming?

An eloquent Jew, Apollos, came from Alexandria and began preaching. He was mighty in the Scriptures, but knew only the baptism of John. Aquila and Priscilla taught him the way of the Lord more perfectly, and sent him on to Corinth (Acts 18:24-28).

112

54. What did Paul accomplish in Ephesus?

His preaching had a profound effect on the city. So many heeded his preaching that people brought their pagan books of magic worth fifty thousand pieces of silver and burned them; they also ceased buying silver images of Diana to the extent that the silversmiths started a riot (Acts 19:8-41).

55. What did Paul do about Apollos' disciples?

He rebaptized them, since they had been baptized only with the baptism of John the Baptist and had not received Christian baptism. This is the only instance in the Bible of anybody who had been immersed having been rebaptized (Acts 19:1-7).

56. Where did Paul go after leaving Ephesus?

He made a trip through Macedonia and Greece and thence to Jerusalem, where he was attacked by the Jews and saved from death by the Roman soldiers (Acts 20:1—23:35).

57. What events followed?

Paul was taken to Cæsarea, the Roman capital of Palestine, where he was held by Felix, the governor, in hopes that Paul's friends would bribe him to release Paul. When a change of governors took place, and Festus succeeded Felix, he, also, tried to gain favor of the Jews by asking Paul to go to Jerusalem to face his accusers, though they had appeared before Felix, and Paul, seeing he would not get justice, appealed to Cæsar (Acts 23:26—25:12).

58. Was Paul reserved for the decision of the emperor?

Yes. Festus, embarrassed at having to send one to the emperor who had committed no crime, called in Agrippa II to assist him in finding a reason to give. Agrippa said he might have been released had he not appealed to Cæsar. The voyage to Rome was a perilous one, which included shipwreck and delay, but Paul arrived safely (Acts 25: 13—28: 29).

59. How does the Book of Acts end?
Paul is awaiting trial in Rome. He has been allowed to hire a house for himself, and there he teaches and preaches to those who come and go. He has been in Rome two years at the close of the account.

60. Did the emperor release Paul?
Yes. Paul continued in the work for about five years. References to the things done are found in 1 and 2 Timothy and Titus.

61. What finally happened to Paul?
Nero became insane and began a persecution of the Christians. Paul was taken prisoner, and this time he knew there was no escape (2 Tim. 4: 6-8). Tradition tells us that, being a Roman, he was beheaded. We are also told that Peter was crucified upside down, feeling he was not worthy of being crucified in the same manner as the Saviour.

62. Was this persecution the end of the church?
No. The church has survived many persecutions, and will continue to do so. Jesus said that even "the gates of hell shall not prevail against it" (Matt. 16: 18).

THE REVELATION

1. Who wrote the Book of Revelation?
The apostle John (Rev. 1: 1).

2. Where was it written.
On the isle of Patmos, in the Aegean Sea, where John had been banished for being a Christian (Rev. 1: 9).

3. With what does Revelation deal?

With the things which were to come to pass in the future (Rev. 1:1); particularly, the times of the end; yet, the past and present were also pictured (Rev. 1:19).

4. Why is Revelation said to be a mysterious book?

Because it is written in symbols.

5. Did the people of that day understand them?

Yes, but many of them we do not understand today. Today, we understand the meaning of "The Blue Eagle," "The WPA," "Uncle Sam," etc. A thousand years from now those symbols may be a great mystery, but they serve us acceptably today.

6. Does that mean that Revelation has no value for us today?

No. The spiritual teachings have a real value, and are clear. Read the messages to the "seven churches" (Rev. 1:11—3:22), the story of the judgment, heaven and hell (Rev. 20:11—22:20). There are many prophecies which are yet to be fulfilled. Some are being fulfilled in our day. We need, however, to guard against speculation on coming events, which disturbs and divides the church.

7. Were there only seven churches in Asia Minor?

No, there were many churches. But these seem to be types of churches, and if we study them, we will find our own church among them, so that the message applies to all that are similar.

8. What lessons stand out clearly?

That churches must be active or die, be loyal or be rejected by Christ.

9. What is the message to the church at Ephesus?

Commendation: They had worked hard and patiently, and had held to the true doctrine.

115

Present Condition: They had "left their first love."

Warning: Repent and do first works or the light would go out.

Promise: "To him that overcometh will I give to eat of the tree of life, which is in the midst of the paradise of God" (Rev. 2:1-7).

10. What is the message to the church at Smyrna?

Warning: They claimed they were poor and having a hard time, but were not. Persecution was ahead which would try them.

Promise: "Be thou faithful unto death, and I will give thee a crown of life . . . He that overcometh shall not be hurt of the second death" (Rev. 2:8-11).

11. What is the message to the church at Pergamos?

Commendation: They were faithful in the midst of persecution.

Warning: Some were becoming immoral and commanded to repent.

Promise: "To him that overcometh will I give to eat of the hidden manna, and will give him a white stone, and in the stone a new name written, which no man knoweth saving he that receiveth it." ("White stone"—God is giving His vote of approval. People used black stones—or balls—when voting against a person.) (Rev. 2:12-17).

12. What is the message to the church at Thyatira?

Commendation: This church had a faithful record in the past.

Warning: A Jezebel, prominent woman worker, was leading some into immorality. "Repent . . . I am he which searcheth the reins and hearts: and I will give unto every one of you according to your works."

Promise: "He that overcometh, and keepeth my works unto the end, to him will I give power over the nations" (Rev. 2: 18-29).

13. What is the message to the church at Sardis?

Warning: They had a name that they lived by (had been faithful in the past), but were now dead; they started things, but never finished them. They must repent!

Commendation: There were still a few worthy.

Promise: "He that overcometh, the same shall be in white raiment; and I will not blot out his name out of the book of life, but I will confess his name before my Father and before his angels" (Rev. 3: 1-6).

14. What is the message to the church at Philadelphia?

Commendation: They had kept His Word and had not denied His name.

Promise: Because they had kept His Word, Christ would be with them in the hour of trial which was soon to come upon the whole world. "Him that overcometh will I make a pillar in the temple of my God (Rev. 3: 7-13).

15. What is the message to the church at Laodicea?

Warning: They were neither hot nor cold, and because they were neither, Christ would spew them out of His mouth.

Promise: "To him that overcometh will I grant to sit with me in my throne, even as I also overcame, and am set down with my Father in his throne" (Rev. 3: 14-22).

16. What is the meaning of the four horsemen of the Apocalypse?

White Horse—Christianity: Christ, the Rider, goes forth to conquer sin and evil.

Red Horse—War: If Christ is rejected, war follows.
Black Horse—Famine and pestilence, which follow war.
Pale Horse—Death, and Hell following (Rev. 6: 1-11).

17. Are there to be only 144,000 people saved?

No. There is to be a great multitude from every nation which no man could number (Rev. 7: 4, 9).

18. What is the meaning of the angel with the little book which was eaten?

The little book is the gospel, and Christ is the Messenger. When the "good news" of the gospel is first received it is very sweet, but when the commands are noted, it becomes bitter to many (Rev. 10: 2, 8-11).

19. Who was the man represented by the beast whose number was 666?

This is supposed to be Nero, the Roman emperor, who was a type of all corrupt rulers and dictators. The Jews did not have figures as we do, but let certain letters stand for figures. So here is the way scholars arrive at the 666:

The Hebrew for Nero	N—	50
Cæsar is NRON KSR.	R—	200
(These are the conson-	O—	6
ants; the vowels were	N—	50
not written in Hebrew	K—	100
with the exception of	S—	60
the "O.")	R—	200

(Rev. 13: 11-18.)   666

20. Where is Armageddon?

This word really means "Mt. Megiddo," which is southwest of the Plain of Esdraelon (Rev. 16: 16),

21. **Is it there that the last battle in the world is to take place?**

It is possible, but Armageddon is more important as the symbol of a great spiritual conflict against the devil and his hosts and those who follow them. The Plain of Esdraelon was a well-known battleground of the Orient.

22. **Describe the judgment scene as pictured to John.**

The dead, both small and great, are standing before the throne of God. The heavenly register, the Book of Life, contains the names of the righteous. "The books" containing the record of individual lives are there, and out of these the dead are judged according to their works (Rev. 20:11-14).

23. **How is heaven described?**

1. As a beautiful city, the New Jerusalem, made ready as a bride adorned for her husband (Rev. 21:2, 9, 10). The walls are of jasper, the gates of pearl, the streets are of gold. A beautiful river flows through the city. And the tree of life is now restored to man (Rev. 21:18—22:2). 2. Jesus described it as a home. "In my Father's house are many mansions . . . I go to prepare a place for you" (John 14:1-4). 3. There will be no more disease, sorrow, death. There will be no need of sun, for the presence of God will give light. This will be the everlasting abode of the righteous (Rev. 22:3-5).

24. **How is hell described?**

1. As a lake of fire and brimstone (Rev. 20:10). 2. As the "bottomless pit" (Rev. 9:1). 3. Jesus also describes it as a place of darkness (Matt. 8:12).

25. **Is not hell a terrible place for men to go?**

It was never intended that men should go there; it was prepared for the devil and his angels (Matt. 25:41). If men are determined to serve him, they must share his fate.

119

DO YOU KNOW THE BIBLE?—No. 1

Do you know the Bible, or are you constantly confusing Scripture with non-Biblical quotations? In this list, part of the quotations are Scripture and part are not. Check the ones you believe to be taken from the Bible.

1. "Man shall not live by bread alone." .... ☐

2. "Death is the golden key that opens the palace of eternity." .... ☐

3. "The child is father of the man." .... ☐

4. "How shall we escape, if we neglect so great salvation?" .... ☐

5. "Truth, crushed to earth, shall rise again." .... ☐

6. "Now faith is the substance of things hoped for, the evidence of things not seen." .... ☐

7. "Let your conversation be without covetousness; and be content with such things as ye have." .... ☐

8. "Even so faith, if it hath not works, is dead, being alone." .... ☐

9. "Faith is the pencil of the soul that pictures heavenly things." .... ☐

10. "If conscience smite thee once, it is an admonition; if twice, it is a condemnation." .... ☐

11. "True repentance is to cease from sinning." .... ☐

12. "One sin doth provoke another." .... ☐

13. "If any man suffer as a Christian, let him not be ashamed." .... ☐

14. "Just as the twig is bent, the tree is inclined." .... ☐

15. "They that be whole need not a physician, but they that are sick." .... ☐

16. "Ye can not serve God and mammon." .... ☐

17. "Judge not, that ye be not judged." .... ☐

18. "The greatest of faults is to be conscious of none." .... ☐

19. "They think too little, who talk too much." .... ☐

20. "Love gives itself; it is not bought." .... ☐

1. **Matt. 4:4.** 2. **John Milton.** 3. **William Wordsworth.**
4. **Heb. 2:3.** 5. **William Cullen Bryant.** 6. **Heb. 11:1.**
7. **Heb. 13:5.** 8. **Jas. 2:17.** 9. **T. Burbridge.** 10. **Nathaniel
Hawthorne.** 11. **Ambrose.** 12. **Shakespeare.** 13. **1 Pet. 4:16.**
14. **Alexander Pope.** 15. **Matt. 9:12.** 16. **Matt. 6:24.**
17. **Matt. 7:1.** 18. **Thomas Carlyle.** 19. **Dryden.** 20. **Longfellow.**

DO YOU KNOW THE BIBLE?—No. 2

Check the quotations from the Bible.

1. "Ye shall know them by their fruits." .... ☐

2. "But he that is greatest among you shall be your
   servant." .... ☐

3. "Repentance, to be of any avail, must work a change
   of heart and conduct." .... ☐

4. "If religion does nothing for your temper, it has done
   nothing for your soul." .... ☐

5. "Little sins are pioneers of hell." .... ☐

6. "Ye generation of vipers, how can ye escape the
   damnation of hell?" .... ☐

7. "Temptations without imply desires within." .... ☐

8. "God can not be tempted with evil; neither tempteth
   he any man." .... ☐

121

9. "Man is tempted, when he is drawn away of his own lust." .... ☐

10. "He who has no mind to trade with the devil, should be so wise as to keep away from his shop." .... ☐

11. "Blessed is the man that endureth temptation: for when he is tried he shall receive the crown of life." .... ☐

12. "No degree of temptation justifies any degree of sin." ☐

13. "When lust hath conceived, it bringeth forth sin; and sin, when it is finished, bringeth forth death." ☐

14. "Temptation in the line of duty, God hath provided for; but for temptation sought and coveted, God has no provision." .... ☐

15. "How immense appear to us the sins that we have not committed." .... ☐

16. "There is no fool equal to the sinner, who every moment ventures his soul." .... ☐

17. "Ye ask, and receive not, because ye ask amiss." .... ☐

18. "Draw nigh to God, and he will draw nigh to you."..... ☐

19. "Remorse is the echo of a lost virtue." .... ☐

20. "Ye are in heaviness through manifold temptations." ☐

1. **Matt. 7: 16.** 2. **Matt. 23: 11.** 3. **T. L. Cuyler.** 4. **Robert Clayton.** 5. **J. B. Howell.** 6. **Matt. 23: 33.** 7. **H. W. Beecher.** 8. **Jas. 1: 13.** 9. **Jas. 1: 14.** 10. **Robert South.** 11. **Jas. 1: 12.** 12. **N. P. Willis.** 13. **Jas. 1: 15.** 14. **G. E. Rees.** 15. **Madam Necker.** 16. **John Tillotson.** 17. **Jas. 4: 3.** 18. **Jas. 4: 8.** 19. **Bulwer.** 20. **1 Pet. 1: 6.**

DO YOU KNOW THE BIBLE?—No 3

Check the quotations from the Bible.

1. "Carry the cross patiently and with perfect submission, and in the end it will carry you." .... ☐

2. "This world is the land of the dying; the next is the land of the living." .... ☐

3. "He who does evil that good may come pays a toll to the devil to let him into heaven." .... ☐

4. "Good deeds ring clear through heaven like a bell."..... ☐

5. "Cowards die many times before their death; the valiant never taste of death but once." .... ☐

6. "O death, where is thy sting? O grave, where is thy victory?" .... ☐

7. "As we have borne the image of the earthy, we shall also bear the image of the heavenly." .... ☐

8. "Cleanliness is indeed next to godliness." .... ☐

9. "Noble examples stir up noble actions." .... ☐

10. "Be ye not unequally yoked together with unbelievers." .... ☐

11. "Whoso findeth a wife findeth a good thing." .... ☐

12. "Who can find a virtuous woman, for her price is far above rubies." .... ☐

13. "As a jewel of gold in a swine's snout, so is a fair woman which is without discretion." .... ☐

14. "If you would have a good wife, marry one who has been a good daughter." .... ☐

15. "It is better to dwell in a corner of the house top than with a brawling woman in a wide house." .... ☐

16. "What therefore God hath joined together, let not man put asunder." .... ☐

17. "Why do ye not rather take wrong? Why do ye not rather suffer yourselves to be defrauded?" .... ☐

18. "I would have you wise unto that which is good, and simple concerning evil." .... ☐

19. "Goodness is love in action." .... ☐

20. "He that is good to another, is also good to himself." ☐

1. **Thomas a' Kempis.** 2. **Tryon Edwards.** 3. **A. W. Hare.** 4. **Jean Paul Richter.** 5. **Shakespeare.** 6. **1 Cor. 15:55.** 7. **1 Cor. 15:49.** 8. **John Wesley.** 9. **Seneca.** 10. **2 Cor. 6:14.** 11. **Prov. 18:22.** 12. **Prov. 31:10.** 13. **Prov. 11:22.** 14. **Thomas Fuller.** 15. **Prov. 21:9.** 16. **Mark 10:9.** 17. **1 Cor. 6:7.** 18. **Rom. 16:19.** 19. **James Hamilton.** 20. **Seneca.**

DO YOU KNOW THE BIBLE—No. 4

Check the quotations from the Bible.

1. "Charity never faileth." .... ☐

2. "If nobody loves you, be sure it is your fault." .... ☐

3. "And now abideth faith, hope, charity, these three; but the greatest of these is charity." .... ☐

4. "Love thyself last." .... ☐

5. "Men must love the truth before they can thoroughly believe it." .... ☐

6. "Keep cool and you command everybody." .... ☐

124

7. "Let every man be swift to hear, slow to speak, slow to wrath." .... ☐

8. "The tongue is a fire; a world of iniquity." .... ☐

9. "If any man offend not in word, the same is a perfect man and able also to bridle the whole body." ...... ☐

10. "He that will love life, and see good days, let him refrain his tongue from evil." .... ☐

11. "Violence in the voice is often only the death rattle of reason in the throat." .... ☐

12. "When a man is wrong and won't admit it, he always gets angry." .... ☐

13. "To rule anger is well; to prevent it is still better.".... ☐

14. "The greatest remedy for anger is delay." .... ☐

15. "He that would be angry and sin not, must not be angry with anything but sin." .... ☐

16. "Let not the sun go down upon your wrath." .... ☐

17. "Abstain from all appearance of evil." .... ☐

18. "Bad men excuse their faults; good men will leave them." .... ☐

19. "Prove all things; hold fast that which is good." .... ☐

20. "Beware lest any man spoil you through philosophy and vain deceit." .... ☐

1. **1 Cor. 13: 8.** 2. **Philip Doddridge.** 3. **1 Cor. 13: 13.** 4. **Shakespeare.** 5. **Robert Smith.** 6. **St. Just.** 7. **Jas. 1: 19.** 8. **Jas. 3: 6.** 9. **Jas. 3: 2.** 10. **1 Pet. 3: 10.** 11. **J. F. Boyes.** 12. **T. C. Haliburton.** 13. **Tryon Edwards.** 14. **Seneca.** 15. **Thomas Secker.** 16. **Eph. 4: 26.** 17. **1 Thess. 5: 22.** 18. **Ben Jonson.** 19. **1 Thess. 5: 21.** 20. **Col. 2: 8.**

Check the quotations from the Bible.

1. "Our conscience is a fire within us and our sins as fuel; instead of warming, it will scorch us, unless the fuel is removed or the heat of it be allayed by penitential tears." ☐

2. "Where your treasure is, there will your heart be also." ☐

3. "A good tree cannot bring forth evil fruit, neither can a corrupt tree bring forth good fruit." ☐

4. "To pity distress is human; to relieve it is godlike." ☐

5. "The love of heaven makes one heavenly." ☐

6. "Forgive us our debts, as we forgive our debtors." ☐

7. "Two persons can not long be friends if they can not forgive each other's little failings." ☐

8. "Life that ever needs forgiveness has for its first duty to forgive." ☐

9. "He that committeth sin is of the devil." ☐

10. "Too low they build who build below the skies." ☐

11. "Perfect love casteth out fear." ☐

12. "No man hath seen God at any time." ☐

13. "If we receive the witness of men, the witness of God is greater." ☐

14. "No man is free who can not command himself." ☐

15. "Every step towards Christ kills a doubt." ☐

16. "If there be first a willing mind, it is accepted according as a man hath and not according to that he hath not." ☐

17. "He which soweth sparingly shall reap also sparingly." .... ☐

18. "God loveth a cheerful giver." .... ☐

19. "God helps them that help themselves." .... ☐

20. "Better limp all the way to heaven than not get there at all." .... ☐

1. **J. M. Mason.** 2. **Matt. 6:21.** 3. **Matt. 7:18.** 4. **Horace Mann.** 5. **Shakespeare.** 6. **Matt. 6:12.** 7. **Jean Bruyere.** 8. **Bulwer.** 9. **1 John 3:8.** 10. **Edward Young.** 11. **1 John 4:18.** 12. **1 John 4:12.** 13. **1 John 5:9.** 14. **Pythagoras.** 15. **T. L. Cuyler.** 16. **2 Cor. 8:12.** 17. **2 Cor. 9:6.** 18. **2 Cor. 9:7.** 19. **Old proverb.** 20. **Billy Sunday.**

DO YOU KNOW THE BIBLE?—No. 6

Check the quotations from the Bible.

1. "Anger begins in folly and ends in repentance." .... ☐

2. "He that is slow to anger is better than the mighty; and he that ruleth his spirit than he that taketh a city." .... ☐

3. "When anger rushes, unrestrained, to action, like a hot steed, it stumbles in the way." .... ☐

4. "A soft answer turneth away wrath: but grievous words stir up anger." .... ☐

5. "Make no friendship with an angry man; and with a furious man thou shalt not go." .... ☐

6. "An angry man is again angry with himself when he returns to reason." .... ☐

7. "When anger rises, think of the consequences." .... ☐

127

8. "Be not hasty in thy spirit to be angry: for anger resteth in the bosom of fools." .... ☐

9. "Let not the sun go down upon your wrath." .... ☐

10. "Title and ancestry render a good man more illustrious and an ill one more contemptible." .... ☐

11. "Cast thy bread upon the waters: for thou shalt find it after many days." .... ☐

12. "The race is not to the swift, nor the battle to the strong." .... ☐

13. "Never trouble trouble till trouble troubles you." ...... ☐

14. "Never meet trouble halfway." .... ☐

15. "Whatsoever thy hand findeth to do, do it by thy might." .... ☐

16. "How much has cost us the evils that never happen!" ☐

17. "Though a sinner do evil an hundred times, and his days be prolonged, yet surely I know that it shall be well with them that fear God." .... ☐

18. "Atheism is the death of hope, the suicide of the soul." ☐

19. "There is no book on which we can rest in a dying moment but the Bible." .... ☐

20. "It is better to hear the rebuke of the wise, than for a man to hear the song of fools." .... ☐

1. **Pythagorus.** 2. **Prov. 16: 32.** 3. **Richard Savage.** 4. **Prov. 15: 1.** 5. **Prov. 22: 24.** 6. **Publius Syrus.** 7. **Confucius.** 8. **Eccl. 7: 9.** 9. **Eph. 4: 26.** 10. **Joseph Addison.** 11. **Eccl. 11: 1.** 12. **Eccl. 9: 11.** 13. **Anonymous.** 14. **John Ray.** 15. **Eccl. 9: 10.** 16. **Thomas Jefferson.** 17. **Eccl. 8: 12.** 18. **Hugh Miller.** 19. **John Selden.** 20. **Eccl. 7: 5.**

DO YOU KNOW THE BIBLE?—No. 7

Check the quotations from the Bible.

1. "He that loveth silver shall not be satisfied with silver; nor he that loveth abundance with increase." ☐

2. "There is no witness so terrible, no accuser so powerful, as conscience which dwells within us." ☐

3. "Conscience tells us that we ought to do right, but it does not tell us what right is." ☐

4. "A man who writes an immoral, but immortal, book may be tracked through eternity by a procession of lost souls from every generation, every one to be a witness against him at the judgment, to show him and the universe the immeasurableness of his iniquity." ☐

5. "Nothing is so easy as to deceive one's self; for what we wish, that we readily believe." ☐

6. "The profit of the earth is for all." ☐

7. "There is a generation that are pure in their own eyes, and yet is not washed from their filthiness." ☐

8. "There is a generation that curseth their father, and doth not bless their mother." ☐

9. "There is no brotherhood of man without the Fatherhood of God." ☐

10. "A man's pride shall bring him low: but honour shall uphold the humble in spirit." ☐

11. "Where there is no vision, the people perish." ☐

12. "Correct thy son, and he shall give thee rest." ☐

13. "Before you beat a child be sure you are not the cause of the offense." .... ☐

14. "The rod and reproof give wisdom: but a child left to himself bringeth his mother to shame." .... ☐

15. "Children have more need of models than of critics." ☐

16. "Tale-bearers are just as bad as tale-makers." .... ☐

17. "While you live, tell truth and shame the devil." .... ☐

18. "A lie that is half a truth is ever the blackest of lies." ☐

19. "The getting of treasures by a lying tongue is a vanity tossed to and fro of them that seek death." .... ☐

20. "Lying lips are abomination to the Lord." .... ☐

1. **Eccl. 5: 10.** 2. **Sophocles.** 3. **H. C. Trumbull.** 4. **G. B. Cheever.** 5. **Demosthenes.** 6. **Eccl. 5: 9.** 7. **Prov. 30: 12.** 8. **Prov. 30: 11.** 9. **H. M. Field.** 10. **Prov. 29: 23.** 11. **Prov. 29: 18.** 12. **Prov. 29: 17.** 13. **Austin O'Malley.** 14. **Prov. 29: 15.** 15. **Joseph Jubert.** 16. **R. B. Sheridan.** 17. **Shakespeare.** 18. **Tennyson.** 19. **Prov. 21: 6.** 20. **Prov. 12: 22.**

DO YOU KNOW THE BIBLE?—No. 8

Check the quotations from the Bible.

1. "It is best to live as friends with those in time with whom we would be to all eternity." .... ☐

2. "A religion without mystery is a religion without God." .... ☐

3. "An honest man is the noblest work of God." .... ☐

4. "The fewer the words the better the prayer." .... ☐

5. "The way of a fool is right in his own eyes." ....☐

6. "The lip of truth shall be established forever." .... ☐

7. "He that withholdeth corn, the people shall curse him: but blessing shall be upon the head of him that selleth it." .... ☐

8. "Riches profit not in the day of wrath." .... ☐

9. "The years of the wicked shall be shortened." .... ☐

10. "The blood of martyrs is the seed of the church." .... ☐

11. "Hasty marriage seldom proveth well." .... ☐

12. "A prudent wife is from the Lord." .... ☐

13. "Whoso findeth a wife findeth a good thing." .... ☐

14. "A youth of sensuality and intemperance delivers over a wornout body to old age." .... ☐

15. "The heart has reasons that reason does not understand." .... ☐

16. "Unstained thoughts do seldom dream on evil." .... ☐

17. "Whoso mocketh the poor reproacheth his Maker.".... ☐

18. "Even a fool, when he holdeth his peace, is counted wise." .... ☐

19. "Make not thyself the judge of any man." .... ☐

20. "A merry heart doth good like a medicine." .... ☐

1. **Thomas Fuller.** 2. **Jeremy Taylor.** 3. **Alexander Pope.** 4. **Martin Luther.** 5. **Prov. 12:15.** 6. **Prov. 12:19.** 7. **Prov. 11:26.** 8. **Prov. 11:4.** 9. **Prov. 10:27.** 10. **Jerome.** 11. **Shakespeare.** 12. **Prov. 19:14.** 13. **Prov. 18:22.** 14. **Cicero.** 15. **J. B. Bossuet.** 16. **Shakespeare.** 17. **Prov. 17:5.** 18. **Prov. 17:28.** 19. **Longfellow.** 20. **Prov. 17:22.**

DO YOU KNOW THE BIBLE?—No. 9

Check the quotations from the Bible.

1. "A foe to God was never a true friend to man." .... ☐

2. "To be doing good is man's most glorious task." .... ☐

3. "A foolish son is a grief to his father." .... ☐

4. "A friend loveth at all times." .... ☐

5. "Look not thou upon the wine when it is red." .... ☐

6. "Be not thou envious against evil men, neither desire to be with them." .... ☐

7. "It will cost something to be religious; it will cost more to be not so." .... ☐

8. "A truth that one does not understand becomes an error." .... ☐

9. "He who would govern others should first be master of himself." .... ☐

10. "There are no crown-wearers in heaven that are not cross-bearers here below." .... ☐

11. "He who prays as he ought will endeavor to live as he prays." .... ☐

12. "Riches certainly make themselves wings." .... ☐

13. "Train up a child in the way he should go: and when he is old, he will not depart from it." .... ☐

14. "He that loveth pleasure shall be a poor man: he that loveth wine and oil shall not be rich." .... ☐

15. "Wine is a mocker, strong drink is raging: and whosoever is deceived thereby is not wise." .... ☐

16. "Earth has no sorrow that heaven can not heal." ▢

17. "Heaven must be in me before I can be in heaven." ▢

18. "There is not a single moment in life that we can afford to lose." ▢

19. "Prayer is a virtue that prevaileth against all temptations." ▢

20. "Pride goeth before destruction, and an haughty spirit before a fall." ▢

1. **E. D. Young.** 2. **Sophocles.** 3. **Prov. 17:25.** 4. **Prov. 17:17.** 5. **Prov. 23:31.** 6. **Prov. 24:1.** 7. **J. Mason.** 8. **A. Desbarolles.** 9. **Philip Messenger.** 10. **Chas. H. Spurgeon.** 11. **J. J. Owen.** 12. **Prov. 23:5.** 13. **Prov. 22:6.** 14. **Prov. 21:17.** 15. **Prov. 20:1.** 16. **Thomas Moore.** 17. **Charles Stanford.** 18. **E. M. Goulburn.** 19. **St. Bernard.** 20. **Prov. 16:18.**

DO YOU KNOW THE BIBLE?—No. 10

Check the quotations from the Bible.

1. "Better is a little with righteousness than great revenues without right." ▢

2. "A word spoken in due season, how good is it!" ▢

3. "Speak not in the ears of a fool." ▢

4. "Any man may make a mistake, but none but a fool will continue in it." ▢

5. "Truthfulness is a cornerstone in character, and if it is not firmly laid in youth, there will ever after be a weak spot in the foundation." ▢

6. "Wicked companions invite and lure us into hell." ▢

7. "Righteousness exalteth a nation: but sin is a reproach to any people." ▢

8. "A good man leaveth an inheritance to his children's children." .... ☐

9. "A conscience void of offense before God and man is an inheritance for eternity." .... ☐

10. "Noble examples stir up noble actions." .... ☐

11. "Keep sound wisdom and discretion." .... ☐

12. "Riches profit not in the day of wrath: but righteousness delivereth from death." .... ☐

13. "Greater love hath no man this, that a man lay down his life for his friends." .... ☐

14. "The difficulty is not so great to die for a friend, but to find a friend worth dying for." .... ☐

15. "It is as sport to a fool to do mischief." .... ☐

16. "The narrow soul knows not the godlike glory of forgiving." .... ☐

17. "It is one of the severest tests of friendship to tell your friend his faults." .... ☐

18. "He that winketh with the eye causeth sorrow." .... ☐

19. "Go to the ant, thou sluggard; consider her ways, and be wise." .... ☐

20. "In all thy ways acknowledge him, and he shall direct thy paths." .... ☐

1. **Prov. 16: 8.** 2. **Prov. 15: 23.** 3. **Prov. 23: 9.** 4. **Cicero.** 5. **J. Davis.** 6. **Henry Fielding.** 7. **Prov. 14: 34.** 8. **Prov. 13: 22.** 9. **Daniel Webster.** 10. **Seneca.** 11. **Prov. 3: 21.** 12. **Prov. 11: 4.** 13. **John 15: 13.** 14. **Henry Home.** 15. **Prov. 10: 23.** 16. **Nicholas Rowe.** 17. **H. W. Beecher.** 18. **Prov. 10: 10.** 19. **Prov. 6: 6.** 20. **Prov. 3: 6.**

INDEX